Peter S. Ford is a physician and surgeon on the medical staffs of two hospitals in Portland, Oregon. He has been a fellow in psychiatry at the Mayo Clinic. In addition to his private practice of medicine, Dr. Ford serves as Clinical Instructor in Family Practice at the University of Oregon Medical School.

THE
HEALING
TRINITY

THE
HEALING
TRINITY
Prescriptions for Body, Mind, and Spirit

PETER S. FORD, M.D.

HARPER & ROW, PUBLISHERS
New York, Evanston, San Francisco, London

FIRST EDITION

LIBRARY OF CONGRESS CATALOG CARD NUMBER: 78–160639

To my wife Barbara
and to our children
Anne
Bronwyn
Marcus
Eric
Paula
and John

Contents

Acknowledgments

If I had any doubts about my dependent nature prior to compiling this book, they have since vanished. It would be impossible for me to list the names of all the people and patients who have contributed directly and indirectly to the formation of this manuscript, but I feel compelled to mention a few of the more obvious contributors. I am indebted to my wife, not only for the proofreading, compositional corrections, and her assistance in compiling the bibliography, but for her cheerfulness during the many long hours of husband neglect. To my office secretary, Emilee Taylor, who typed and retyped this manuscript so many times, a special note of thanks. I wish also to express my sincere appreciation to five distinguished members of the theological profession: First, to Dr. Albert C. Outler, who despite his own superhuman schedule reviewed this manuscript and made many helpful suggestions in its final composition. And to Chaplain William F. Adix, Dr. Laurence P. Byers, the Rev. L. Raymond White, and the Rev. Vernon A. Groves, who in friendship and professional dedication have critically reviewed this book in its intermediate stage of development. Finally, a note of gratitude to my oldest son, Marcus, who is currently preparing for graduate study in theology, for his inspiration, contemporary thought, and creative suggestions.

P.S.F.

Prologue

For the past several years, I have participated as a physician in a chaplaincy-training program at one of the local metropolitan hospitals. The program seeks to assist ministers to fulfill their supporting role in the treatment of hospitalized patients. When I first undertook the work I thought that my job was merely to acquaint clergymen and seminary students with a few of the medical problems they would encounter in their hospital ministry. I emphasized anatomical, physiological, and biochemical changes that occur within the diseased body, for I rather naïvely thought that the ministers were interested in medicine only so that they could talk more knowledgeably with patients and physicians. I had also assumed that the primary task of the hospital minister was to visit each patient, read some appropriate Scripture, perhaps offer a prayer, and then politely leave.

I soon discovered, however, that many ministers were not content with this stereotyped role; they really wanted to become more actively involved in the care of the patients. They wanted to know more about both the nature of organic illness and the current modes of medical therapy. In addition, they became intensely interested in the psychological manifestations of illness: the patients' anxieties, strengths, hopes, and depressions. Because many of the ministers had academic training and experience in pastoral psychology, some of them began to assume the role of psychological counselor. Often their interpretation of the psychodynamics and psychopathology conflicted with those given the patient by the attending physician. As a result, tensions grew, tempers flared, and frustrations developed between the physicians and the clergymen, leading to a situation that proved detrimental to both.

I was caught in the middle. On the one hand, I agreed with the attending physicians, whose primary responsibility was the care and treatment of the patient. On the other hand, I could not help but recognize that the clergy were overly restricted to perfunctory duties. They obviously had more to offer than they were allowed to give, and we of the medical profession were making them feel like "second-class citizens." How the clergymen could participate more actively in patient care without elements of competition and professional conflict was a problem to which neither side had yet given adequate thought. The basic issue was: What should be the role of religious faith in the treatment of emotional and physical illness?

As I worked to develop a program which would bring the special capabilties of both physicians and clergy to the best service of the seriously ill, I was confronted with the complex nature of the problem. Where does psychological illness end and spiritual illness begin? What delineates these two conditions in a patient suffering from an emotional illness? Is spiritual illness really a separate disease entity? Should the clergy minister only to the patient's spiritual needs and not get involved in any of the psychological aspects of the illness? I did not feel that I could answer adequately any of these profound and stimulating questions.

But I was persuaded of their urgency, for, after being in the private practice of medicine for nearly ten years, I had noticed that there was an increasing frequency of mental and emotional illness in my daily practice. I had gradually become acutely aware of the psychological elements that accompanied nearly every major organic illness. Patients suffering from coronary occlusion almost always developed profound depressive reactions. Patients afflicted with cancer often died prematurely, not because of physical complications, but because they had lost the will to live. I was intrigued by the high incidence of postoperative psychosis, especially in the open heart cases, and wondered if there were ways of preventing the patient from losing contact with reality after prolonged surgery.

I also became impressed by the many patients who repeatedly sought help for minor medical complaints. Some, indeed, had mild forms of chronic organic illnesses, but most were of a functional or psychosomatic nature—or at least so I thought. Upon closer questioning and observation, I began to see a common denominator in each of these illnesses. Nearly all such patients lacked any appreciable joy, direction, or purpose in living. At first I attributed this to the fact that their ailments were chronic—they were becoming "unintentional hypochondriacs," pathetically attempting to find an organic explanation for their fatigue, headaches, insomnia, loss of appetite, and frequent colds.

Few of the patients were willing to accept a diagnosis of psychoneurosis or functional illness as the cause of their malady. Most would insist that I was overlooking something in their physical examination or laboratory tests that would validate the organic nature of their illness. Others would frankly state that I was mistaken in my diagnosis. A rather high percentage of these patients would move on to another physician, attempting to find someone who would provide an acceptable organic diagnosis. My initial reaction to the loss of these patients was a defensive one; I told myself that I didn't really care where they went. Then I began to feel that I had failed to meet their real needs through my own lack of insight. And so I decided to interrupt my practice of medicine and resume training in psychiatry.

I entered my fellowship in psychiatry with enthusiasm. When I was not treating patients or attending lectures and seminars I read as much psychiatric literature as I could consume. I participated in nearly every group therapy session that was available, worked part time in the community mental health center, and visited the deeply disturbed patients in the closed wards of a state mental institution. But in less than a year I realized that psychiatry, per se, offered very little in the way of definitive therapy for such people. I was discouraged and woefully depressed, although I knew that psychiatry unquestionably contributes more to the care and treatment of mentally ill people than any other therapeutic discipline currently available.

What I did discover was that many of the patients who suffered from vague somatic and emotional symptoms were not mentally ill at all, at least not in the usual academic or diagnostic sense. Most of these people were spiritually ill, that is, they were suffering from the results of rejection and prolonged periods of love-deprivation. It was not only human love that they were lacking; they were separated from the love of God. I knew that I had ultimately to turn to theology to learn about the interaction of love and evil that are so strongly present in this form of human suffering.

The late Dr. Paul Tillich was the primary inspiration of my pursuit of a spiritual therapy for spiritual illness. His genius ignited me in a manner both indescribable and unparalleled in my entire life. His writings seemed clear, concise, and courageous. They opened up new vistas of theological thought and revelation. He made religion seem both real and relevant, and his profound knowledge of psychological principles and dynamics gave for me a special vitality and dimension to his religious writings. I think that Tillich, more than any other theologian, has lessened the gap that has so long existed between theology and psychology. He has managed on numerous occasions to bridge the chasm between them in such a manner as to neither dilute nor distort the uniqueness of either discipline.

While I was working in this field, it became apparent to me that I was attempting to reach at least three specific groups. First were the clergymen who had invited me to participate in their chaplaincy training program and who had initially stimulated my interest in spiritual therapy. By virtue of their academic background, theological orientation, and experience with the healing potential of God, I feel that nearly all members of the clergy are in the favored position to grasp the need for spiritual therapy.

Second were my medical colleagues and those actively engaged in clinical psychology. I felt that they should become aware that spiritual illness is a common form of human suffering or disease. Its uniqueness lies not in its isolation from other forms of disease, for this is seldom the case, but in the fact that its origin and therapeutic dynamics differ significantly from those of all other organic and mental illnesses. I wanted to develop a special type of therapy specifically designed to assist those suffering from spiritual illness and struggling in its grip, and to make psychologists as well as clergymen understand its usefulness.

To those already afflicted with the torment of spiritual illness, and to their loved ones, I wished to offer the assurance that life is not futile or their malady incurable. I wanted to tell them that God can and does heal and that there is a genuine hope of health and wholeness for those who earnestly seek his love.

And so I continued my research in the hopes that a method could be discovered by which spiritual illness—that illness which arises from man's separation from God—could be effectively treated. This volume is the result of my work.

Peter S. Ford

Portland, Oregon

To outward appearance, the modern world was born of an anti-religious movement: man becoming self-sufficient and reason supplanting belief. Our generation and the two that preceded it have heard little but talk of the conflict between science and faith; indeed it seemed at one moment a foregone conclusion that the former was destined to take the place of the latter.

But, as the tension is prolonged, the conflict visibly seems to need to be resolved in terms of an entirely different form of equilibrium—not in elimination, nor duality, but in synthesis. After close on two centuries of passionate struggles, neither science nor faith has succeeded in discrediting its adversary. On the contrary, it becomes obvious that neither can develop normally without the other. And the reason is simple; the same life animates both. Neither in its impetus nor its achievements can science go to its limits without becoming tinged with mysticism and charged with faith. In short, as soon as science outgrows the analytic investigations which constitute its lower and preliminary stages, and passes on to synthesis—synthesis which naturally culminates in the realization of some superior state of humanity—it is at once led to foresee and place its stakes on the future and on the all. And with that it out-distances itself and emerges in terms of option and adoration.

PIERRE TEILHARD DE CHARDIN[1]

THE
HEALING
TRINITY

1

Three Dimensions of Suffering

Mrs. D. was a 38-year-old, white, married female. Her chief complaints were weight loss, abdominal pain, and an inability to sleep. Her symptoms had been present for nearly three months. She had lost fifteen pounds and had noticed a change in bowel habit manifested by frequent liquid stools that, on occasion, contained some bright red blood. Furthermore, she often experienced cramping pain in her lower abdomen. Her family history revealed that her father died at 47 from a primary carcinoma of the stomach. Her mother, age 62, was alive, but residing in the state mental institution where she had been for the last ten years. She was allegedly suffering from an "involutional melancholia." The patient's social history disclosed that she was married to a Presbyterian minister and during their 16 years of marriage had had four children ranging in age from 6 to 14 years. She was a college graduate from the state university and had majored in music and minored in psychology.

She confided to me that she was afraid that she had developed cancer of the stomach like her father, and for that reason she had delayed seeking medical attention. Furthermore, she was beginning to wonder if she were slipping mentally and feared that she might end up in a pyschiatric ward like her mother. A complete physical examination was carried out, including x-rays, sigmoidoscopic and basic laboratory tests. A battery of blood studies was also undertaken in order not to overlook any blood dyscrasia or metabolic abnormalities that might be the cause of her symptoms. All tests were found to be well within normal limits. No evidence of cancer or other disease processes were found to account for her weight loss, abdominal pain, or change of bowel habit.

When I confronted her with this good news, instead of being happy and overjoyed, she reacted in just the opposite manner. She told me that she really didn't think I would find anything wrong with her, at least not of an organic nature. She told me that her problem was far more serious than cancer and that she didn't suppose anything could be done to help her. After that hopeless declaration came a flood of tears, followed by a long moment of silence. Finally, an account of what was really troubling her began to pour out.

Mrs. D. had commited adultery with a member of her husband's congregation. She had done it during a moment of sensual impulse and at a time when she was feeling sorry for herself. Apparently her husband had been so busy becoming "successful" that he had failed to fulfill his wife's physical and emotional needs. So, while attending a conference in a neighboring city, she had met this man and succumbed to the temptation of physical attraction and her desire for sexual satisfaction. Her guilt feelings were tremendous. It was quite obvious that they were rapidly destroying her physically, mentally, and spiritually. She hadn't the courage to tell her husband what she had done, for she couldn't be sure how he would react. She also had the children to think of, for legally an act of infidelity could give the father legal custody of all the children. The patient said she loved her husband and had no desire to divorce him for the other man. The patient further admitted that she had received psychiatric help prior to coming to the clinic, thinking that it would give her solace and relief from her suffering. Her initial therapist had diligently reassured her that extramarital affairs were quite commonplace and that she was overreacting to what she had done. He had tried to convince her that there was now a new morality that gave the individual a greater latitude in his sexual expression, one which was designed to reduce and not to increase sexual tensions. Furthermore, the therapist had suggested that she not tell her husband because it would only compound her problem and would make her husband suffer needlessly. This counseling had proven helpful only for a short period of time. Now she felt even more guilty than before. She had to lie to her husband about spending money for other things while all the time she was paying for psychiatric treatment. Moreover, she was anxious about having to explain to her husband that she was not organically ill at all but was suffering from some form of psychoneurosis.

At first I tried to handle this case in the usual psychotherapeutic manner. I initially delved deeply into her past life, especially her childhood and earlier developmental years, to see if I could find any previous pattern of depressive reactions or periods of psychological disturbance. I found none. I searched for evidence of significant love-deprivation during her years at home with her parents and while attending school and college. I found none. I also looked for indications of significant rivalry between herself and her five younger siblings. There was none. She had had a happy childhood with no major calamities. She had not come from a broken home. Her parents had been happily married, well educated, reasonably successful, and well adjusted by all prevalent social standards. However, after the rather sudden and premature death of her father, her mother had gone into a deep depression. She had been hospitalized intermittently for several years, but finally had become totally refractory to all modes of psychiatric treatment and was eventually committed for residence at a state mental institution. This was the only appreciable flaw that I could find in her family history.

Through specific questioning, I discovered that her parents had been "very religious" and had made a concerted effort to raise their children in a church-oriented environment. I next probed into her sex life, but could find no evidence of psychosexual distortion or abnormalities. She had never been frigid or repulsed by sexual intercourse. She repeatedly averred that she loved only her husband and that they had usually, if not always, enjoyed a high level of mutual sexual compatibility. But she did state that she resented the many evenings her husband would spend attending meetings and doing pastoral visitation. She said she felt at times that she occupied the bottom rung on his ladder of priorities. It became apparent that this was one area of obvious clinical significance. She also expressed a mature and sincere love for her children and had no conscious awareness of hostility or resentment toward any of them.

In spite of all my probing and listening, her problem seemed not to be resolving or her suffering abating. As a matter of fact, in many ways her general condition was getting worse. Her bouts of diarrhea were becoming more frequent. Her appetite remained depressed and she had regained only two pounds of her lost weight. Moreover, her days and nights were equally fitful in spite of generous dosages of tranquilizers, mood elevators, and bedtime sedation. She could barely keep up with her housework. She could take care of only the most urgent needs of her husband and children and had virtually withdrawn from all church activities. I was becoming increasingly concerned over her lack of progress and her poor state of health. Finally, I realized I had to discard my nondirective role and adopt a more active and positive attitude.

I began by first confirming what she already knew: that she was getting no better. I then told her that I thought she could no longer continue to use all of her emotional and psychic energy to repress her attitude of hostility toward her husband and her feelings of guilt over her sexual escapade without suffering possible irreversible damage to her physical and mental health. I asked that she tell her husband about her feelings of hostility, what she had done, and then ask for his forgiveness. Furthermore, I told her that she must realize that this revelation might result in a permanent severance in their marriage relationship, but it was a risk she had to take. Next, I told her that I wanted to refer her to a gastroenterologist to make sure that I had not overlooked any organic disease process during the course of her physical examination that might account for the persistence of her abnormal digestive symptoms. Mrs. D. carried out all of these requests. She told her husband about her angry thoughts toward him and about her extramarital experience. Much to her utter surprise and relief, he forgave her. Furthermore, he had been able to diminish her guilt and hostility toward him by admitting that he, too, had to assume some of the responsibility because of his failure to fulfill her physical and emotional needs. The gastroenterologist confirmed my previous diagnosis of an "irritable colon syndrome," but stated that she was beginning to develop early signs of ulcerative colitis. He placed her on a more stringent diet than I had recommended and added more potent medication.

From these new therapeutic innovations, Mrs. D. began to show almost immediate improvement. She started to regain her appetite and put on weight. Her daytime and evening medication requirements began to diminish and she soon became able to resume more of her duties as a wife, mother, homemaker, and assistant to the minister. She seemed to be well on her way to recovery.

But I had run up the victory flag too hastily. For within three months she was again beginning to show signs of emotional and physical deterioration. Her depression returned as did her diarrhea, anorexia, weight loss, fatigue, and insomnia. In addition, she had developed two more symptoms: vomiting and intractable head-aches. Because she could no longer maintain an adequate fluid level, she was admitted to the hospital and fed intravenously. She was put back on all of her previous medication but this time in even higher doses. I even arranged that she be temporarily isolated from her family to see if they were in any way contributing to her recur-rent illness.

It was not until the second week of her hospitalization that I was able to uncover the reason for the exacerbation and prolongation of her illness: it lay in her relationship to God. It was her inability to seek God's forgiveness and to accept herself and what she had done that was her major obstacle to recovery. Even though her husband had genuinely offered her his forgiveness, she had not really been able to accept it. Mrs. D.'s insoluble problem resided in her religion. She had a limited and distorted view of God and his love. She had been raised, as her history pointed out, in a very religious environment. She had attended Sunday school and church with rigid regularity and had assimilated large and frequent por-tions of fundamental theology. This produced a warped concept of the Judeo-Christian tradition to the point where the Gospel was antiscientific, antisocial, and almost antihuman. In this interpreta-tion, the sins of the flesh were found to be the worst kind of offense against God; they were the ones that almost defied forgiveness and tended to damn one to an eternal hell.

It was this fear of eternal damnation that finally erupted and provided the critical clue to Mrs. D.'s illness. Because of the gravity of her situation and because I had been able to develop a close rapport with her, I momentarily stepped out of the role of the physician and told her that God was kinder and more gracious than she had ever supposed. I told her that there was no unfulfilling act (sin) so great that God could not forgive it. Furthermore, I exceeded my professional authority and suggested what she needed most was to ask and accept God's forgiveness.

She was able to accomplish this, though not at that moment. But she did accomplish it while she was still in the hospital. And from that time on her healing began. After three months she was completely restored physically, mentally, and spiritually. Mrs. D. is now living a joyful and productive life beside her husband and in the midst of her children.

This case clearly reveals the three dimensions of human suffering and demonstrates the need for the combined skills of the physician, psychologist, and clergyman. Unfortunately, interprofessional teamwork is seldom utilized in the diagnosis and treatment of human maladies. This therapeutic deficiency must no longer be ignored or remain uncorrected.

Until recently, the dictum that doctors treat but God heals had proved sufficient. Today, however, most men want to know more about how God heals. And it appears that God is equally anxious for man to discover some of these mysteries that will afford him comfort, hope, and healing.

The biochemists and nuclear physicists have unraveled one of the greatest enigmas concerning the nature of life by discovering the DNA and RNA molecules. Virologists and bacteriologists are learning how microorganisms affect normal cell metabolism and give rise to many forms of human disease. Pharmaceutical chemists are finding new ways to synthesize antibiotics that will kill or inhibit the growth of bacteria, viruses, and fungi that threaten human health. Surgeons, with the help of immunologists, are learning how to prolong life through organ transplant or by installing mechanical devices that will restore vital physiologic and metabolic functions.

Now the theologians, clergy, and religiously oriented laymen are exploring different aspects of the Christian faith to see if new modes of treatment can be found to alleviate one of the most common forms of human suffering: spiritual illness. It was during such a search that a method of diagnosis and treatment called *telotherapy* was discovered. As this analytical and therapeutic approach to spiritual illness is developed, I hope that it will eventually stand beside medicine, surgery, psychiatry, and clinical psychology as a unique form of therapy in the healing arts. Its uniqueness and complementary status will become apparent as its dynamics and precepts are described. Telotherapy, per se, is not new; only its name is different. A similar and superior method of treatment was introduced nearly two thousand years ago by Jesus of Nazareth. Yet this special healing power that Jesus used so frequently has virtually lain dormant and has all but disappeared today. A few vestiges of it—some genuine, but most ineffective and flagrant distortions— have appeared from time to time. But to my knowledge, no systematic or methodical attempt has been made to construct a rational discipline that would have significant therapeutic application in contemporary twentieth century society.

In recent years many elements have stimulated the formation of telotherapy. Without a doubt, the two greatest motivating forces for its development were the recognition of spiritual illness as a complex disease entity and the awareness that this condition could be diagnosed and effectively treated. And it has been through the efforts of such a man as Paul Tillich, in his *Systematic Theology* and other writings, that the dynamics of man's essential nature and his existential dilemma were clarified. Tillich clearly outlines the mission of the church as well as delineating man's fulfilling and therapeutic relationship with his Creator.

Other factors have provided additional impetus. Foremost among these have been the development of diagnostic and therapeutic psychiatry and psychology. These two closely allied disciplines (which should be considered as one in terms of a similar apprehension of psychodynamics) have provided us with an enormous amount of information regarding the normal growth and development of the human mind and personality. Furthermore, they have brought forth a clearer understanding of the distortions of mental and emotional health that manifest themselves in varied clinical forms of mental illness. The revelation of the many psychodynamics that influence human health and happiness are invaluable in helping man achieve mental and emotional equanimity.

A recent but inadvertent influence exerted by psychiatry on telotherapy was the honest admission on the part of a few renowned psychiatrists of their inability to effectively treat every form of emotional illness. This gave rise to two speculations: first, that there were certain forms of emotional illness that seemed to be highly refractory to the usual modes of psychological treatment; and, second, that not all forms of emotional illness were necessarily psychological in nature.

Dr. Carl Jung provides us with an excellent illustration of this point. He says,

I am reminded of a case which is very instructive in this connection. It concerns a highly intelligent young man who had worked out a detailed analysis of his own neurosis after a serious study of medical literature. He brought me his findings in the form of a precise and well-written monograph fit for publication, and asked me to read the manuscript and to tell him why he was not cured. He should have been according to the verdict of science as he understood it. After reading his monograph I was forced to grant him that, if it were only a question of insight into the casual connections of a neurosis, he should in all truth be cured. Since he was not, I supposed this must be due to the fact that his attitude to life was somehow fundamentally wrong—though I had to admit that his symptoms did not betray it. In reading his account of his life I had noticed that he often spent his winters at St. Moritz or Nice. I therefore asked him who paid for these holidays, and it thereupon came out that a poor school-teacher who loved him had cruelly deprived herself to indulge the young man in these visits to pleasure resorts. His want of conscience was the cause of his neurosis, and it is not hard to see why scientific understanding failed to help him. His fundamental error lay in his moral attitude. He found my way of looking at the question shockingly unscientific, for morals have nothing to do with science. He supposed that, by invoking scientific thought, he could spirit away the immorality which he himself could not stomach. He would not even admit that a conflict existed, because his mistress gave him the money of her free will.[2]

The pursuit of this obvious gap in modern psychology revealed what we are about to discuss. I discovered that much of what had formerly been labeled as psychological illness was indeed spiritual illness. I also found that these people require entirely different therapy to modify or to heal their illness than that offered by standard modes of psychiatric practice. But this discovery should in no way detract from the effectiveness of psychotherapy in the treatment of many forms of emotional and mental illness. It should only make us aware that there is no single antidote for all the various kinds of emotional infirmities that afflict mankind. Telotherapy in no way competes with psychology any more than psychology competes with medicine. Both are necessary for the fulfillment of man's happiness and wholeness.

I should also mention some of the negative factors that have impeded the devlopment of telotherapy. One is the failure or reluctance on the part of most therapists within the psychological persuasions to recognize the spiritual element within every human being and, more specifically, within every patient they treat. I do not wish to imply that all patients who suffer from a psychological illness may also be suffering from a spiritual illness, although I suggest that this possibility cannot be completely ruled out. I am merely asking that all psychologists and psychiatrists at least acknowledge the fact that man is a composite of body, mind, and soul, and that the possibility of spiritual illness is real. A letter I received from Tillich shortly before his death verifies this observation.

It may interest you to know that the psychiatric department at the University of Chicago has asked me to have a regular seminar with members of their staff about the problems of the doctrine of man in [the] theological and psychotherapeutic view. Just about the day on which your letter arrived, we had a two-hour discussion which centered around the question you ask, namely, my distinction of man's essential nature and existential estrangement. Most of the medical men tried, just as you indicate, to *reject* the idea of an essential nature.

A second deterrent to the formation of telotherapy was found within the ranks of the clergy. Many ordained ministers and priests had been innocently wooed and beguiled by the language and techniques of certain psychotherapists and analysts, and were reading theological implications into these psychological methods that did not exist. Jung describes a facet of this problem when he says,

The fact that many clergymen seek support or practical help from Freud's theory of sexuality or Adler's theory of power is astonishing, inasmuch as both these theories are hostile to spiritual values, being as I have said, psychology without the psyche (soul). They are rational methods of treatment which actually hinder the realization of meaningful experience. By far the larger number of psychotherapists are disciples of Freud or of Adler. This means that the great majority of patients are necessarily alienated from a spiritual standpoint—a fact which cannot be a matter of indifference to one who has the realization of spiritual values much at heart.[3]

He goes on to say,

It is well known that Freudian psychoanalysis is limited to the task of making conscious the shadow-side and the evil within us. It simply brings into action the civil war that was latent, and lets it go at that. The patient must deal with it as best he can. Freud has unfortunately overlooked the fact that man had never yet been able single-handed to hold his own against the powers of darkness—that is, of the unconscious. Man has always stood in need of the spiritual help which each individual's own religion held out to him.[4]

In the light of these two statements, it would be a grave mistake for clergymen to assume that much of applied psychology and psychiatry are in harmony with the basic doctrines of the Christian faith. At the present time this is simply not the case.

Another example of what could be called the "great deception" within the minds of many clergy is found in the writings of Erich Fromm, especially in *The Art of Loving* and *Psychoanalysis and Religion*. In the first book he writes, "Analytic therapy is essentially an attempt to help the patient gain or regain his capacity for love." This means the "ability to love productively, to love without greed, without submission or domination, to love from the fullness of his personality."[5] As keen an observation as this is and as fine a pronouncement as this may seem Fromm fails to recognize the immutable fact that God alone is the source of this love and that man is incapable of generating love by his own power. Furthermore, he fails to realize "the fact that divine and human love cannot be fulfilled apart from each other."[6]

So beneath this thin and deceptive veneer of apparent accord lies the age-old problem of *humanism* and *naturalism* versus *theism*. Only the clothes and accoutrements have changed. Both may be using the same words but they are not speaking the same language, for a subtle but significant polarity still exists. "Naturalism," says Outler,

is man's declaration of independence and sovereignty in the world which he measures and values for himself. Theism is man's acknowledgment of radical dependence upon God and his finitely-free responsibility as creatures and citizens of God's beloved community. . . . Naturalism stands for love as the highest human virtue; theism for love as God's greatest gift to man and His highest will for man."[7]

The difference in these concepts of love is clear, they are not synonomous in character.

A third negative feature has been the concerted effort, perhaps more unconscious than conscious, on the part of a few theologians and members of the clergy to "Christianize" psychology or to "psychologize" Christianity. Both tasks are equally impossible and all such efforts are destined to fail. Psychology is an academic discipline that stands among the other members of the behavioral sciences: anthropology and sociology. Christianity can only hope to affect the lives of behavioral scientists and perhaps influence their application of this acquired knowledge. But neither Christianity nor any other theology should ever attempt to modify or distort another body of knowledge for its own purpose. Theologians and psychologists must be motivated to explore the depths of their own academic persuasion and be willing to share the secrets of their discoveries with others. There is a recognized interrelatedness and interdependency between all of the disciplines of human learning, and especially so between psychology and theology.

Periodically, it becomes necessary to reassess the limits of each academic field and see which borders need to be expanded and which, if any, need to be diminished. I think that with the introduction and application of telotherapy the need to expand the boundaries of theology will become imperative. But this expansion must not be at the expense of psychology, which must also continue to grow in its understanding of the psychodynamics of the human organism and make even greater contributions toward alleviating human suffering. But it would be wrong to assume that there has been little or no exchange of information. Quite the contrary. Several outstanding intellectual giants have freely shared their particular wisdom with those in the adjacent camp, preeminent among whom are such men as William James, Carl Jung, and Gordon Allport in psychology. And from theology have come such notable teachers as Paul Tillich, David Roberts, and Albert Outler. Each of these remarkable educators has not only been a distinguished pioneer within his own field, but each has been willing to explore the broad gray area that arbitrarily separates these two cognitive persuasions.

It is important to mention the impact of existential philosophy upon telotherapy. Existentialism is currently enjoying an acme of popularity. Many scholars have arbitrarily attempted to divide the major contributors to this philosophy into two general categories: those who are atheistic and those who are theistic in their basic assumptions and presentations. According to this description, men such as Sartre, Marx, and Nietzche would be classified as atheistic existentialists, whereas Kierkegaard, Marcel, and Buber would be considered theistic existentialists. But in the strictest sense this division is spurious, for existentialism deals only with the analysis of what it means to exist. However, it is when these same philosophers attempt to answer the questions generated by their own analytical thought that the impulse to place these qualifying labels upon their work becomes irresistible. The philosopher who utilizes a humanistic approach to resolve existential questions would, I suppose, be considered atheistic, and one who incorporates the dynamics of theological thought would be considered theistic. Therefore, telotherapy would most specifically address those who, by this extraphilosophical distinction, are the acknowledged advocates of atheistic existentialism. It would offer them a contemporary theological solution to the many problems basic to the human dilemma. Instead of *No Exit,* as espoused by Sartre, telotherapy would offer an opening. Instead of futility, as implied by Camus in his *Myth of Sisyphus,* telotherapy would offer hope.

2

Spiritual Illness

Spiritual illness may be defined as an emotional and cognitive malady that arises out of the human failure to respond to God's love. It results in a three-way separation: a separation of the individual from God, from himself, and from others. In the context of our analysis of the dynamics of spiritual illness, we will see that rejection and love-deprivation are synonymous, and that separation is the usual result of rejection. Spiritual illness differs from spiritual immaturity only insofar as the degree of separation, or the amount or period of love-deprivation has not yet significantly interfered with the individual's happiness and his ability to function adequately in his environment.

There are many clinical signs and symptoms of this malady, and they are often present in a manner similar, if not identical, to many forms of psychological illness. This is quite understandable since the individual must use the same modes and channels for expressing his spiritual sickness as he does his psychological illness; namely, through a disturbance in his cognitive and his emotional apparatus. This admittedly makes the process of differentiating between spiritual and mental illnesses difficult. But the etiologic factors of spiritual illness are often vastly different from those of mental illness, and therefore our approach to their prevention and treatment will differ considerably.

A similar confusion exists in medicine. It is often very difficult, if not frequently impossible, to separate functional (psychological) from organic conditions. Two common examples come to mind. First, there is the patient who comes to the physician complaining of episodic chest pain with radiation of this pain into his left shoulder and down his left arm. He may be suffering from coronary artery disease and could be experiencing genuine anginal attacks. Or he may be suffering from a "cardiac neurosis," which can mimic coronary artery disease in nearly every detail. One can readily see the importance of differentiating between these two conditions. True angina implies a potentially serious condition. But anterior chest wall pain that has a neuromuscular or skeletal origin or is a manifestation of tension and fatigue carries a much brighter prognosis. Hence an accurate diagnosis becomes imperative before any rational treatment or assurance can be given.

A second example is the patient who suffers recurrent headaches of increasing severity and duration. This pain could be the result of tension, migraine, vascular disease, a brain tumor, or numerous other conditions. The physician must determine if the headache represents a life-threatening condition or if it is something of a benign nature that constitutes little serious risk. And so it is with the person who comes seeking help with his emotional problems. It must first be ascertained if his symptoms arise primarily as the result of separation and unfulfillment due to an absence of or inappropriate response to God's love, which would indicate the presence of a spiritual illness, or if he was suffering from the results of an unresolved psychosexual conflict suggesting the presence of a mental illness. Then it would be imperative to determine the seriousness of his disease and decide what method of treatment should be best applied and by whom.

It would be nice to suppose that all medical and psychological diagnoses are clear-cut. They are not. Nor, as we shall see, are they in telotherapy. Both medicine and psychiatry have gone beyond the either-or concept in both diagnosis and treatment, and hopefully the same will be true in this application of clinical theology. That is, a physician seldom attempts to explain all of the patient's symptoms solely on the basis of *either* an organic *or* a psychological disturbance. Rather, the doctor tries to determine how many of the presenting symptoms—e.g., pain, loss of appetite, and weakness—are a direct result of organic illness and how much can be attributed to the patient's emotional response to his disease. We have come to recognize that, in the strictest sense, nearly all diseases and ailments that afflict the human organism affect all three facets of the human triad—body, mind and soul—to a greater or lesser degree. And the principle challenge of diagnosis and treatment alike is to determine which facet or facets are predominatly afflicted and which segment or segments need the greatest and most immediate attention. With this in mind, you can see that it is very possible for spiritual illness to be present along with a psychological illness and be in conjunction with an organic illness as well.

Severe forms of spiritual illness are often characterized by a sense of hopelessness and despair. Life for the sufferer has lost both meaning and direction. Some describe their feelings in terms of "absolute emptiness," others as "extreme loneliness." Additional symptoms would include profound feelings of guilt, fear of death or threat of nonbeing, and the feeling of being unloved and unwanted. One of the most vivid descriptions of profound spiritual illness is found in the Book of Job. "Why did I not die at birth, come forth from the womb and expire?" "Why is light given to him that is in misery, and life to the bitter in soul, who long for death, but it comes not, and dig for it more than hid treasures; who rejoice exceedingly, and are glad, when they find the grave?"[8] And perhaps many of the miracles of healing recorded in the New Testament might have been predominantly spiritual illness masquerading in organic and psychological array.

Another example of spiritual illness can be found in Harry Haller's soliloquy of despair in Hesse's *Steppenwolf.*

The passing years had stripped me of my calling, my family, my home. I stood outside all social circles, alone, beloved by none, mistrusted by many, in unceasing and bitter conflict with public opinion and morality; and though I lived in a bourgeois setting, I was all the same an utter stranger to this world in all I thought and felt. Religion, country, family, state, all lost their value and meant nothing to me any more. The pomposity of the sciences, societies, and arts disgusted me. My views and tastes and all that I thought, once the shining adornments of a gifted and sought-after person, had run to seed in neglect and were looked at askance. Granting that I had in the course of all my painful transmutations made some invisible and unaccountable gain, I had had to pay dearly for it; and at every turn my life was harsher, more difficult, lonely and perilous. In truth, I had little cause to wish to continue in that way which led on into ever thinner air, like the smoke in Nietzsche's harvest song. . . . Let suicide be as stupid, cowardly, shabby as you please, call it an infamous and ignominious escape; still, any escape, even the most ignominious, from this treadmill of suffering was the only thing to wish for. No stage was left for the noble and heroic heart. Nothing was left but the simple choice between a slight and swift pang and an unthinkable, a devouring and endless suffering. I had played Don Quixote often enough in my difficult, crazed life, had put honor before comfort, and heroism before reason. There was an end of it![9]

In most cases of severe spiritual illness, the flame of joy has been extinguished and the zest for living is gone. Suicidal thoughts are common and attempts, both successful and unsuccessful, are plentiful. So the seriousness of this disease should not go unrecognized or the amount of human suffering be minimized. To those trained only in psychology and psychiatry, the diagnosis of chronic agitated reactive depression would seem more appropriate, and nearly every patient with spiritual illness seems to have many of the cardinal features of this disturbance. Yet it would appear that it is the cause and not the manifestations of this emotional-cognitive disease that differentiates the spiritual from the psychological ailment. But the line is indeed a fine one that separates these two forms of human suffering, and I'm not at all sure that a complete distinction can always be made. Even the frankly psychotic person strives to realign himself with God, as is shown by the frequency with which religious symbols present themselves in his art and conversation.

Spiritual illness is the antithesis of spiritual health. Spiritual health is the result of a coalescing unification of the essential dimension of life with the existential. It results from significantly overcoming the triple estrangement that can exist within any finite creature.

The dynamics of spiritual health and spiritual illness reside almost entirely between the action and interaction of two opposing forces: acceptance and rejection. From this we can easily construct a therapeutic proposition or law to express some of the characteristics of these two forces when they operate within the context of human and divine love: "To be accepted is to be loved, and to be loved is to be accepted." And its negative corollary would read, "Not to be accepted is not to be loved, and not to be loved is to be rejected." The first statement relates the dynamics of spiritual health, whereas the second expresses the dynamics of spiritual illness.

It is believed that rejection is the primary cause of most, if not all, spiritual illness. Rejection, in some form or another, is responsible for man's triple separation. But this rejection occurs on many levels and within each of three categories: rejection by and of others, rejection of self, and rejection of God. All contribute to spiritual illness, but the rejection of God, which takes the form of failing to respond to his love, is the preeminent cause of all spiritual sickness.

It is difficult to determine precisely where the cycle of rejection begins within any given individual. And it is equally difficult to ascertain in any one case the relative proportion each category of rejection contributes to the whole of the individual's suffering. I would suppose that in most instances, spiritual illness begins as the result of rejection by those in one's immediate environment: a parent, a sibling, a spouse, a friend, a teacher, a colleague, or an employer. Or, in many circumstances, it might prove to be society in general that is the major rejector, as is so often true with members of a minority group.

However, regardless of who initiates the rejection, the person rejected reacts with feelings of hurt and anger. And this hurt and anger takes on the form of objective hostility, a hostility that wants to "strike back" or "get even" with those who have rejected him. This hostility can express itself verbally, nonverbally, or physically. But each expression of hostility on the part of the rejected individual only serves to further augment the rejection by those who began the cycle. The initiator heaps even more hurtful and devastating forms of rejection upon the wounded individual. And so the circle goes: rejection breeding hostility and hostility reacting in a "getting even" response, which in turn stimulates more punitive reaction by the original tormentor. As a result, the rejected individual either becomes increasingly more violent or learns to acquiesce to the demands or the rejection of his tormentor by suppressing or repressing his feelings of hostility. But suppressed or repressed hostility is not dissipated; it continues to create havoc on both a conscious and unconscious level within the person. And it is these very feelings of objective hostility that both psychology and theology feel are major contributors toward mental and spiritual illness.

We also know that a significant number of people are themselves the instigators of this rejection phenomenon. They are loved, appreciated, and encouraged by thoughtful and mature parents, siblings, teachers, spouses, colleagues and friends, but they choose not to respond appropriately to this love and attention. In these cases, the person seems purposely bent upon making himself the target for rejection, by refusing to accept the love offered to him. Yet it really doesn't matter if the rejection is originated by the individual or by those in his environment—the end result is usually the same. The human reaction toward rejection is eventually to reject those who reject you. Sooner or later, the individual manages to separate himself from others.

Each of us constantly needs confirmation of our own worth. Rejection by others begins the erosion of our concept of self-worth. An absence of this essential validation makes any concept of self-worth virtually impossible and negates any opportunity for developing self-confidence or self-respect. In extreme cases of environmental rejection, a concept of self-worth is never nurtured, and the individual has little or no self-confidence or self-respect to lose. But whether the loss is great or small, the terminal effect is almost always the same: the individual ends up disliking himself. Out of defense and sheer desperation, he will often create a fantasy or unreal concept of himself within his own mind that is substituted for his unacceptable real self. By the time this occurs, the individual has become separated from himself. Both psychology and clinical psychiatry have detailed the effects of self-rejection upon the human organism in their literatures.

The third and final form of rejection is seen in man's rejection of

God. I will place a great deal of emphasis on the many ways man chooses to separate himself from his Creator, and will examine in some detail the several modes of rejection responsible for his separation from God.

Because the thesis and theology upon which telotherapy is predicated maintains that one of the major causes of spiritual illness arises from man's separation from God, we should explore some of the many origins for this particular kind of separation. But first it is important to note that there are two different forms of separation from God, primary and secondary. In either condition, there is never complete separation from God; it is always relative. There is nothing, says the apostle Paul, that man can do or fail to do that will ever irrevocably or unequivocally separate him from the love of God. Neither, however, is there ever total unity with God in this life, even though many men have strived to attain it. The Christian faith affirms that the only exception was Jesus of Nazareth, who was the Christ.

Primary separation is present at the time of conception and birth. It is the condition of all human life. Primary separation is intrinsic in our creaturehood and was so planned by God. The challenge of existential life is to voluntarily overcome this estrangement between self and God, thereby making it possible for us to accept ourselves and others. According to Tillich, this primary separation is man's basic sin. Sin, singular, and with a capital 'S,' says Tillich, is separation from God. Plural sins, with a small 's,' would be anything that would increase or perpetuate this separation.

At this point, however, I would eliminate Tillich's use of the word sin in both instances, but not his concept. I feel that the common idea of sin has outlived its usefulness and persists as an emotional, if not an intellectual, barrier for many Christians and non-Christians alike. I would substitute the term *unfulfilled* to convey the inherent existential situation of man. One could then say that man is created in a state or condition of unfulfillment, which is an expression of his separation from God. We could then replace the idea of "sinning" with the more contemporary concept of "committing unfulfilling acts." In this way we would eradicate the repelling traditional theological term of sin with all of its dreadful judgmental overtones and replace it with a more acceptable and less demeaning expression.

Primary separation, per se, is seldom the direct cause of spiritual illness. It might best be considered a state of spiritual immaturity. However, if this spiritual immaturity persists throughout adult life, the individual will be rendered susceptible to the forces of secondary separation, which indeed provides the principle source for all spiritual illness. So one must actively develop his spiritual potential in order to protect himself against these secondary factors. In other words, spiritual maturation provides a very significant immunity from the ravages of the many forms of spiritual illness.

Secondary separation is anything that widens the primary gap between man and God which was present at birth, or that prevents the closing of this intrinsic schism. Chief among these factors causing secondary separation are: ignorance, pride, apathy, evil, and demonic forces. All of these must be considered as human or extrahuman forces that cause a rejection of God by man. Let us consider in more detail some of these factors.

Ignorance

Ignorance concerning the spiritual dimension of life is much greater than is supposed. Although most people have some general ideas about God and the Christian faith, they are extremely lacking in the fundamental concepts of Christian theology. Most people have not only an immature grasp of the basic concepts of their relationship to God, but they also have a very minimal and distorted concept as well. To compound this major deficiency, these same people often build an elaborate but flimsy superstructure upon this inadequate foundation and spend most of their lives trying to prevent its collapse. The more vocal ones in our society are generally considered to be religious fanatics. But there are many reasons for this theological ignorance.

First, there is an insufficient number of adequately trained personnel to teach the doctrines and dynamic concepts of the Christian faith on all educational levels. Second, it has not been possible to make theology a part of the required curriculum in the public schools, colleges, and universities. Third, people resist learning theological principles because they feel that religion is either optional, unnecessary, irrelevant, or perhaps threatening. And fourth, there is a perpetuation of the fallacy that religion is both intuitive and private, and therefore, that Christianity in its deepest insights and faith requires little or no formal teaching or rational understanding.

It is a recognized fact that within the framework of the Christian faith there are not enough professionally trained theologians, professors of religion, ministers, priests, or Christian educational directors to do the job that must be done. There is also an obvious deficiency in the utilization of these highly trained individuals. Most theologians and professors of religion spend a very small proportion of their time teaching. Much of their energy is siphoned off in other directions that drastically diminish their teaching potential. And those who do teach are usually limited to seminaries and small private colleges, with little opportunity to penetrate so-called secular institutions.

The predicament of the pastoral minister and priest is even greater. He is expected to be administrator, fund-raiser, counselor, spiritual inspiration, and teacher for groups of often recalcitrant and indifferent parishioners. Furthermore, he is expected to change their lives through the single medium of a Sunday morning sermon. This sermon must be stimulating, nonoffensive, witty, profound, biblical in origin, and with minimal contemporary application so as not to disturb the minds of the more generous supporters of the church's operational budget. Moreover, the minister must also relate equally well to people ranging in age from 7 to 70 with varied educational backgrounds and interests.

The Christian educational director has many of the same problems as the priest and minister, but he is not encumbered by as many duties or by the need to assuage every church member. He is an authority in his field by virtue of his academic training and title. In many ways he commands more respect than the minister, even though his educational background is not as extensive. His primary job is to mobilize an adequate number of people from the ranks of the church membership to participate in the teaching program. He must often flatter and cajole these people to keep them active in the program despite the fact that their contributions to the process of communicating religious knowledge leaves much to be desired. These laymen constitute the fourth teaching source of Christian doctrine. Some are very capable, others woefully inept. And insofar as most of the laymen are unpaid volunteers, neither the minister nor the directors of Christian education have complete control over the teaching situation. Even with the help of good educational material, there is little assurance that what is actually taught adheres to the truths found within the curriculum. Most often the untrained volunteer is equipped only with good intentions and will teach what arises out of his own meager theological background. So the problem is compounded when we realize that this poorly equipped lay teacher may provide the only source of religious education that many individuals may ever receive.

A fifth and final factor that further contributes to this problem of Christian ignorance and confusion is the lack of academic standardization in the field of Christian theology. There are a certain number of schools that are founded more out of zeal and rebellion than out of a desire to further academic excellence. This condition is markedly intertwined with the whole problem of denominationalism, especially within the Protestant church. There are altogether too many "Biblical seminaries," "Bible colleges," and "Bible schools" turning out graduates who are willing in spirit but lacking in fundamental theological knowledge. As a result, their interpretations of the gospel and Christian doctrine often deemphasize the need for any rational comprehension of theology, Church history, or spiritual maturity, and thereby produce additional impediments to genuine understanding.

Thus, is it any wonder that so many people have such a limited and distorted concept of the dynamic relationship that exists between man and God? These inadequate modes of education must be altered in order to eliminate such theological ignorance.

Pride

The second and perhaps the single greatest factor that prevents victory over our separation is pride. This pride is also known as self, ego, *hubris*, or arrogance. It is the existential "I" that stubbornly refuses to relinquish ultimate control of the self to God. Pride is the rejection of God in favor of self. It is especially difficult for people who have been brought up in a competitive capitalistic society to give up anything. We feel what we have earned is justly ours, our money and everything material we possess. Even the factor of time becomes possessively ours, as do our very selves. Our arrogance knows no limits.

So it is through choice, if not ignorance, that we become egocentric instead of theocentric individuals. And herein lies the basic human error. We were not designed to be self-centered but God-centered creatures. Yet within the expanse of our relative or finite freedom, which is an integral part of the condition of creation and human existence, we are given an option to choose between these two centers of living. Some choose to be self-centered because they are ignorant and do not realize that they have a choice. They assume that all people are self-centered like themselves, and the idea of a God-centered individual is incomprehensible and defies their rationality. Furthermore, these people become suspicious of anyone who claims to hold to any center other than themselves. But most of us who are self-centered have chosen this path. We don't want to relinquish our position of power. We want to stay in the center of the stage of life and push God toward the perimeter.

Finally, we are reluctant to live God-centered lives because genuine humility would dictate that we give God credit for our human accomplishments instead of taking credit upon ourselves. Reinhold Niebuhr states unequivocally that pride (self) is man's basic sin and it, more than anything else, is responsible for man's failure to over-come his separation from God. And we know that the very essence of our pride and intransigent behavior arises out of "the human will and desire that God should not exist."[10]

But the difficult thing about being a follower of Christ, actively seeking realignment with God, is that it requires Kierkegaard's "leap into faith." It demands a leap that for a moment completely severs us from everything we know to be real and secure in our existential environment. The God-centered life always requires more than a man is capable of giving, without God's help. And rejecting God's love deprives us of the opportunity to develop or to regain our spiritual health.

Apathy and Indecision

Not to decide is to decide.—HARVEY COX

Apathy and indecision may not represent separate adverse enti-ties, but rather may reflect a combination of factors in which igno-rance, pride, and evil again play a role. Yet they are often inhibiting influences in our society, and so they are cited here as among the many factors that contribute to the secondary separation from God. Passivity of thought and action represent appreciable factors in preventing the process of dealienation from taking place. At least some of the elements which contribute to this attitude should be enumerated.

First, there is an assumption concerning the irrelevance of the Christian faith in contemporary society. In recent years little empha-sis has been placed upon what the Christian faith has had to say about ethics, morality, interpersonal relationships, and human re-sponsibility. The mere recitation of the Ten Commandments and the Golden Rule or some vague reference to the Sermon on the Mount is no longer adequate, if it ever was. Christianity must spell out much more precisely its total realm of concern as well as its ethic for participation within the human society. Furthermore, instead of perpetuating a negative morality that is only concerned with limited and peripheral areas such as smoking, drinking, and illicit sexual activity, Christianity must come forward with positive statements concerning the full scope of human conduct and define the necessary qualities of the mature follower of Christ. In his book *Situation Ethics*, Joseph Fletcher offers a new morality predicated—not upon the legal interpretation of civil and religious laws or upon local mores—but upon a workable ethic based upon *agape* love. This is a notable step in the right direction.

And the scope of Christian concern must also encompass threats to human existence, such as thermonuclear war, mass starvation, drug abuse, pollution in all forms, overpopulation, and the possible clash between the white, black, and yellow races of the world. Though one cannot condone smoking, excessive drinking of alcoholic beverages, or promiscuous sexual activity, with all of their multiple centrifugal effects, when viewed from the perspective of the total human dilemma, they are not the major problems that threaten our society. But these other larger problems must be solved in order for mankind to survive. The rear guard, theologically conservative and literalistic branches of the church, have for too long been preoccupied with the minutiae of ecclesiastical detail, doting inordinately over the carnal sins of man. This segment of the church has remained blind to the larger, secular problems that threaten man's existence. It is not unlike the mother of the bride who dwells over the limited physical attractiveness of her future son-in-law rather than pondering if he will be able to give her daughter adequate love, stability, and inspiration. Unless these literalistic, legalistic, and moralistic branches of Christianity become involved in the major issues, Christianity will remain irrelevant and will contribute to the indifferent attitude that many people have toward the Christian faith as a whole.

A second part of the apathetic attitude toward Christianity is the disillusionment that many have had with those who call themselves Christians. The sting of Mahatma Gandhi's statement, "I like your Christ, but I don't like your Christians," is still being felt today. This criticism is well founded. The term "Christian" is used so loosely and glibly that any person who attends church, confesses to a casual belief in God, or has his name on the membership rolls of a church calls himself a Christian. Seldom is any attempt made to distinguish between a perfunctory church member and an individual who wholeheartedly embarks upon a unique way of life that has both transforming and healing qualities. Hence it appears that most people who call themselves Christian seem to be little different from those who are non-Christian. The frequent incongruity of the successful businessman who exploits his employees and customers alike while serving as a lay leader in his local church is too often true.

A third element of indifference is the repeated disappointments many have experienced when they have gone to the church seeking solace for their suffering. Instead of strength and comfort, they have found trite sermons, meaningless music, and a general attitude of unconcern. Even the minister seems more interested in the visitor's potential financial support rather than meeting his spiritual condition.

A fourth impediment can be attributed to the lack of dynamic leaders and persuasive advocates for the God-centered life. Man's apathy will never be challenged by a scant number of elocutionists backed by a host of lackluster, pious people, who flaunt their "Christian" badge on Sunday, but who are not willing to offer assistance to their suffering neighbor during the rest of the week. Nor will society be challenged by Christians who are so engrossed with their churchmanship and religiosity that they remain insensitive to the many who reside within ghettos, slums, and reservations. If Christianity does not become involved in the suffering of mankind, it becomes a little more than a farce, a fantasy, or an interesting philosophy that stands in direct contradiction to everything that Jesus taught and lived.

A fifth and final factor, which perhaps exceeds all others in perpetuating a passive attitude toward overcoming alienation and establishing a right relationship with God, is our supreme preoccupation with self. We expend nearly all of our working time, thought, and energy trying to achieve the highest possible degree of financial security, social recognition, and self-comfort. The need for resolving an abstract spiritual predicament simply does not make a discernible mark upon our daily priorities. If one views life only from an existential perspective, this attitude is fine. But it is the resolved spiritual life that gives meaning to the existential life, and our search for the unambiguous life will never be successful until we overcome our separation from God.

Evil

Much of the mystery surrounding this major deterrent to attainment of the unified life has remained unsolved and is therefore poorly understood. Yet verification of its existence is legion.

Evil might be defined as the forceful antagonist of good, or as anything that hinders, impedes, or obstructs God's desire to fulfill human life. Evil is a principle factor in the perpetuation of man's triple alienation and frequently stands in the way of health and fulfillment. Our knowledge of evil presumes a knowledge of what is good. Ultimately, evil will only be better conceived as our comprehension of good increases. Evil must also be understood as being antidivine as well as anything that hinders man's quest for an unambiguous life. To impede man from gaining fulfillment is to insult and to antagonize the Creator.

Even a cursory analysis of evil will reveal that it has two main categories: human evil and natural evil. Human evil can be simply divided into its three logical compartments: 1) personal or individual evil, 2) social or combined evil, and 3) historical or inherited evil. Each form actively participates in preventing man from achieving fulfillment not only in a spiritual sense, but often in a mental or physical sense as well.

Human Evil

1. Personal or Individual Evil Man is born with the potential for doing either good or evil. This is part of the condition of his creation and part of the phenomenon of man's finite freedom. It is not the will of God that man chooses to do evil, yet God gives man freedom of choice and, therefore, allows evil to exist within the universe. Preeminent among the various forms of personal evil is that common and redundant element, human pride, or hubris. This is manifested as a desire to place ourselves on an equal or superior footing with God. Pride is the desire for total or infinite freedom, not relative or finite freedom. Pride becomes man's myopic, self-centered preoccupation with life that stands out in direct opposition to the panoramic, God-centered concept of being. Pride includes the will for power, the will for avarice and self-indulgence, and the motivation to kill if personal supremacy, possessions, or survival is threatened. Closely related to human pride are prejudice, discrimination, wickedness, and idolatry. A further demonstration of individual evil is the willful infliction of suffering upon others, which could ultimately lead to their destruction as well as to our own.

2. *Social and Combined Evil*   While all the attributes of personal evil apply here, social evil is more than the mere addition of the various forms of personal evil. The combined capability of evil for two individuals far exceeds that of merely doubling the potential of one. This is evident by observing rioting and other forms of mass violence. Social or combined evil, therefore, becomes a tremendous local, state, national, and international force, a force that stands in direct opposition to the fulfillment of the intentional will of God. Social evil gives rise to racial discrimination and segregation. It creates extreme power and wealth for a few and devastating poverty and social insecurity for many. Combined evil spawns civil and international wars and makes possible the climate for total annihilation of the human race. It quickly becomes apparent what a formidable force social or combined evil can be within our existential society.

3. *Historial or Inherited Evil*   This form includes the symbolic original evil of Adam and Eve in their willful disobedience of God when they partook of the fruit of the tree of knowledge in the Garden of Eden. And we, too, are constantly tempted to use our limited knowledge

to rise above God in order to escape his demands as well as to deny his very existence. Historical evil includes all the aggressive and destructive tendencies that are perpetuated through families, clans, tribes, and nations. It includes all physical defects that are genetically transmitted from one generation to the next, as well as diseases or the proclivity toward developing certain diseases that could impair growth, health, and happiness. The evil of illegitimate births is a commonly overlooked example of inherited evil.

Natural Evil

Natural evil encompasses such occurrences as earthquakes, floods, famines, droughts, hurricanes, tornadoes, and blizzards. These natural events are not the intentional will of God but result from certain partially comprehensible natural phenomena. Until a scant hundred years ago it was thought that disease or pestilence was also a form of natural evil. But once the origins of many diseases had been discovered and their modes of transmission understood, much of the mystery and fear was stripped away, and the connotation of evil has all but been erased. The same is also becoming true about some of these natural phenomena. Even now it does not seem incomprehensible that man will soon be able to control or at least modify many of these physical elements to a degree where they will pose little of their current threat. Already man is well on his way toward insulating himself against climatic extremes. He can build dwellings that are virtually earthquake- and tornado-proof. He will soon be able to prevent flooding and have adequate water reserves for times of drought.

As man continues to unravel the mysteries of the universe the number of natural evils will diminish. However, man's greatest threat will come from unnatural evils, which are of human origin and cannot be attributed to the phenomena of natural forces. These man-made evils, many of which have already been mentioned, take the form of thermonuclear explosives with all of their potential for sudden and unlimited human destruction; pollution of the air, land,

and water with its more insidious threat to human survival; and the present and future reality of overpopulation, which predictably causes plagues and mass starvation for millions of God's creatures. These three factors, more than any others, threaten the existence of mankind. They are the result of individual and social evil, not a manifestation of natural evil.

Demonic forces represent an even more abstract and elusive form of impediment to man's fulfillment. Demonic forces are not only antidivine but often appear deceitfully divine under many circumstances. These forces can cause a spiritual schizophrenia that can substantially inhibit movement toward the unambiguous life. Reinhold Niebuhr provides a lucid description of demonic activities:

> The possession of the self by something less than "holy spirit" means that it is impossible for self to be partly fulfilled and partly destroyed by its submission to a power and spirit which is greater than the self in its empiric reality but not great enough to do justice to the self in its ultimate freedom. Such spirit can be most simply defined as demonic. The most striking, contemporary form of it is a religious nationalism in which race and nation assume the eminence of God and demand unconditional devotion. This absolute claim for something which is not absolute identifies the possessing spirit as "demonic"; for it is the nature of demons to make pretentions of divinity just as the devil "fell" because he sought the place of God. The invasions and possession of the self by spirit, which is not the holy spirit, produces a spurious sense of transfiguration. The self is now no longer the little and narrow self, but the larger collective self, of race or nation. But the real self is destroyed. The real self has a height of spiritual freedom which reaches beyond race and nation and which is closer to the eternal than the more earthbound collective entities of man's history. Such demonic possession therefore destroys and blunts the real self and reduces it to the dimensions of nature. [11]

Biblical mythology suggests that the devil was a fallen angel who was expelled from heaven for attempting to become equal with God. The Apocalyptic book of Enoch and the Old Testament book of Isaiah refer to this fallen angel as Lucifer. This same Lucifer, now the devil, reportedly resides in the realm of Hades where he constantly and tenaciously exerts an evil influence upon the human organism. Many people still cling to a literal interpretation of this concept of the origin of evil. Moreover, they assume that the devil is an autonomous power only slightly less powerful than God. On the surface it would appear that this would be a plausible explanation for the source of man's evil. But closer scrutiny reveals that this dualistic concept creates more theological problems than it solves. Furthermore, it would diminish man's responsibility for his proclivity for evil and pose the sticky question of another deity. Perhaps it would be acceptable to view these demonic powers as a composite of all forms of evil (human and extrahuman) that temporarily resist and distort both the love and will of God, but that ultimately are never successful in their bid to capture the human soul.

So spiritual illness occurs, through one or many of these factors. Let us look at the dynamics of telotherapy, which is designed to help heal this illness.

3

Telotherapy

Love must become man's ultimate concern—not wisdom, wealth nor power. Fortunate people are those who are loved; unfortunate people are those who are not loved. It is these unfortunate ones who become sick within their bodies, minds and souls, for no human can find health or happiness unless he is loved. But man's fulfillment comes in loving God, self and others.[12]

Telotherapy is both a means and an invitation to spiritual healing. The term telotherapy is derived from the Greek *telos,* which means "inner aim" or "ultimate goal." The avowed purpose of this therapeutic method is to assist people who are suffering from spiritual illness to overcome their separation from God and to move toward their ultimate goal of fulfillment. Telotherapy, therefore, becomes a means by which the health of the soul can be restored and the torments of spiritual suffering relieved. Even upon closest scrutiny, telotherapy will be found to be neither a gimmick nor a specious therapeutic device. It uses *agape,* the love of God, as the primary souce of power for all of its healing and acknowledges this to be present in every phase of its therapeutic process. Furthermore, this discipline for spiritual healing is predicated upon the faith and ╰ belief that God is always willing to bestow his healing love upon man. It is only man's ignorance, pride, apathy, evil, or certain demonic forces that prevent him from accepting this divine therapeutic power. Therefore, one of the fundamental goals of therapy is to assist the patient in overcoming these obstacles to God's healing love in order for him to achieve spiritual health and move toward fulfillment.

Telotherapy falls easily, if not spontaneously, into two functional categories: analytical and therapeutic. The analytical phase determines the nature, extent, and the dynamics of the spiritual disease process, when and if present; the therapeutic phase provides the necessary mode of treatment for the amelioration of the existing spiritual malady, should it be discovered. Obviously, the analytical phase would usually preceed any therapeutic effort.

The Analytical Phase

The following systematic analysis makes possible the important differentiation between spiritual and mental illness.

It would seem to follow logically that if there are three component parts to this emotional-cognitive syndrome we call spiritual illness, any adequate method of investigation would have to include a separate analysis of each of these salient segments. This analytical process includes three separate but closely interrelated investigative efforts: an existential analysis, an essential analysis, and an essential-existential analysis. Each division of this triple analysis makes a special contribution to the total analysis. By adhering stringently to this sequential method of investigation, at least in the beginning, most therapists will find that this system of analysis provides the highest yield of pertinent information necessary to establish a diagnosis. Moreover, this order of exploration usually offers the least threat to the patient seeking assistance.

1. Existential Analysis   Existential analysis is the therapist's evaluation of the patient's response to his existence. It measures two primary aspects of the individual's suspected illness: his degree of separation from himself and from others. Modern psychology has long been recognized as the pioneer and the authority in this type of investigation, for psychology concerns itself almost exclusively with the existential dimension of man. On this point, telotherapy freely admits its dependency upon psychology both for its wisdom and for its refined techniques. Yet the existential analysis used in the course of applied telotherapy differs rather markedly from the usual psychological approach.

This analysis is divided into six steps. If properly developed, they should provide the investigator with an optimal overview of the patient's existential situation.

The first step evaluates the limits of the patient's environment. Is he concerned only with the things close to him or does his interest include his community, the state, the nation—the broader scope of things? The second step should assist the patient in exploring the contents of his environment. The therapist should help him to assess which persons and other things are important to him. All significant interpersonal relationships should be probed and evaluated. Attempts should be made to determine how this individual relates to his spouse, his parents, his children, his employers and his peers. To whom does he relate best? With whom does he feel most at ease? Who are his friends? Who are his enemies? What makes him happy, angry or sad? How well does he accept criticism or correction from those in authority or from his peers? Does he have reverence, irreverence, or an indifference towards life?

The third step in this existential analysis focuses upon the patient's attitude toward society in general as distinct from the specific interpersonal relationships probed in the second step. What does he think about the system of city, state, or national government? How does he feel about the restrictions or limitations that society places upon him, especially moral and legal restraints. Is he proestablishment, antiestablishment, or just indifferent? How does he substantiate his position? Is he concerned about people in general or only in people in particular? Is he concerned about such social issues as racial discrimination and the inequitable distribution of wealth? How does he feel about other forms of social injustice, or war, or crime, or environmental pollution?

A fourth step is the patient's self-evaluation. How does he see himself, both as an individual and as a member of society? Does he accept himself or would he rather be someone else? How does he view his intellect, his sexuality, his physical prowess, and his attractiveness? Would he rather be a girl than a boy, a woman than a man, a wife than a husband, or a mother rather than a father? Does he consider himself to be honest, ethical, religious, fair, wise, perceptive, generous, kind, and loving? If not, why not? If so, why?

The fifth step evaluates the patient's value system. It is always clinically rewarding to discover what is important to the individual who comes seeking your help. An earnest attempt should be made to place these things of meaning and worth to the patient in sequence, with the most important items at the head of the list and the least important at the bottom. This short exercise in specific probing frequently reveals a great deal about the patient. Ask him who he wishes most to impress: his family, his friends, himself, or his therapist?

The sixth and final step centers upon the individual's goals and his understanding of the meaning and purpose of life. For many patients, this line of investigation will seem redundant, a repetition of the previous step. To others, it will seem vague and abstract and difficult to apprehend. Some patients feel uncomfortable because they cannot come up with what would seem to be an acceptable answer. It is amazing how few people view life as having either meaning or purpose. But most people respond to these questions in a predictable manner. If the patient is a married woman with a family, she will usually say that her highest ambition is "to be a good wife for her husband and a good mother for her children." And if the patient happens to be a married family man, he will echo the same sentiments, substituting "husband" for wife and "father" for mother. However, most men will place their desire to excel professionally and their need for social recognition ahead of devotion to their family by a significant margin.

Occasionally, telotherapists will find yet another group of patients who will respond somewhat differently to these last questions. They will be individuals who have developed a theological perspective to their understanding of life. They will answer these key questions by saying that their highest ambition in life is "to do the will of God" or "to serve mankind." These particular questions are purposely placed in this sequence in preparation for a smooth transition into the next investigative phase, that of essential analysis.

2. Essential Analysis   Essential analysis is metaphysical both in nature and in concept. It is difficult to grasp. It attempts to measure the third and most important ingredient within this triad of spiritual illness: the quality of the relationship between the individual and God. Essential analysis undertakes the task of determining the level of the patient's awareness of God and the nature of his response. But it must be kept in mind that if the patient has no concept of God, he can have no concept of his "ought." "Ought" is the human realization of the need to respond to God's love. The spirit or soul is that part of man which responds to the divine love of God. Deep within each of us lies an inherent and intuitive awareness of God upon which we can build our sense of "ought." Unfortunately, many people choose not to develop this primitive intuition of God and, as a result, it remains dormant in its primordial state throughout the entire existential life span of these individuals. Happily, there are some who decide to react in a creative and positive fashion to divine love and place it at the center of their lives. Theoretically, the purpose of all organized religion and theology is to help the individual to increase his awareness of God, perfect his concept of "ought," and assist him in his struggle for spiritual maturation. Obviously, few of these man-made institutions ever achieve all of these goals, but it still remains their expressed intent to strive in this direction.

There are no direct ways to measure an individual's essential characteristics: his awareness of God, his sense of "ought," or the exact nature of his response to God's love. Yet, there are several indirect means that can yield valid information in this vital area of analysis. These methods are unsophistocated, but they are sufficiently dependable as to derive reliable data about an individual's human-divine relationship. Perhaps, however, it would be wise at the outset to discard some of the unreliable indicators used in the past for this type of evaluation. It will not come to most as a new revelation to learn that there is very little correlation between one's ability to recite large quantities of scripture, pray well in public, or to actively participate in erudite discussions on various aspects of Christian doctrines or other world religions, and one's closeness to or distance from God. Each of these varied achievements represents an exercise of the mind and does not necessarily express feelings that are within the heart. Nor does there seem to be much convincing evidence that people who attend church, either regularly or irregularly, are any closer to God than those who choose not to participate in corporate worship. As a matter of fact, there is mounting evidence that suggests just the opposite to be true. Those who attend church may actually be farther from the Ultimate Reality. If we cannot use these examples as yardsticks to determine an individual's true religious status, what can we rely upon?

We find that the individual's concept of God offers significant clues. Questions are formulated that evoke certain answers that will assist the therapist to grasp the patient's apprehension about the nature of God and that will give valuable aid in determining the intellectual level of his religious perspective. It would be interesting to learn if the patient's idea of God follows along the lines of J. P. Phillips's description of immature and unreal gods, which take on the form of a "Resident Policeman," a "Grand Old Man," a "Parental Hangover," or a "Heavenly Bosom," as he cleverly outlines in his book *Your God Is Too Small.* Or does the patient have a mature, though not necessarily articulated or scholarly concept of God, who for him permeates all of life and whose presence is a living reality?

Does the patient seem only to know about God but really not know him? Does he have only a vicarious religious sentiment handed down to him by his parents or one foisted upon him from the pulpit? When and how does he pray? What is the usual content of his prayers? Do you detect within your patient much love, empathy, compassion, and concern for others? Does he exude any kindness? These are but a few of the more reliable indicators available to us in making our essential analysis. If the investigation leaves the therapist with the impression that his patient really knows God and has love and concern for his fellow man, he can rightly assume that his patient's malady is not of a spiritual nature.

But if, on the other hand, the patient can only verbalize about God, even though he may be steeped in theological knowledge, and if the therapist can find little or no evidence of love and compassion for others but only anger and self-pity, this patient is spiritually sick. It should be noted that this same patient may also be suffering from a concomitant mental illness, as is so often the case, but this should not dissuade the telotherapist from adhering to his diagnosis of spiritual illness. In other words, the diagnosis of spiritual illness never excludes the possibility of a coexisting mental illness or vice versa. Any competent telotherapist should be able to recognize and evaluate this frequent and challenging situation. In instances where these two forms of emotional-cognitive illness are present, both must be treated, but preference must be given to the sickness that offers the larger threat to the individual's total health and happiness.

I would like to insert at this point that it has been wrongly assumed for too long and by too many that those who are spiritually mature and live in close union with God are thereby immune from the ravages of mental illness. This is not true. Nor are those who are spiritually rugged protected against developing organic disease. Anyone can be afflicted with mental or organic illness. The same holds true for spiritual illness. But there is now significant evidence that suggests that people who suffer from mental illness, but who have a high level of spiritual maturation, have an infinitely better prognosis than the mental patient who lacks this close affiliation with God, for they are better equipped to work through the torments of their illness. It has also been noted that those who suffer from spiritual illness are more prone to develop mental illness. But, again, it does not follow that those who suffer from mental illness necessarily lack a right relationship with God.

Nothing in our discussion has touched upon the requisites of the telotherapist himself. It should, however, be apparent by now that only those who themselves have experienced the love of God in their own lives will be able to perceive the presence or absence of God in the lives of others.

3. Essential-Existential Analysis   This third and final portion of the total analysis becomes an exercise in comparisons. It compares the content of the essential analysis with that of the existential in order to determine the level of the patient's spiritual maturation. This can be accomplished by evaluating the degree of unity that exists between the individual's essential "ought" and his existential "is." Or, to express it more simply, it is a matter of matching a person's potential for fulfillment against his actual performance. The area between the "ought" and the "is" is called the zone of separation. The status of the individual's spiritual maturity is therefore reflected by the width of this zone. If this area is narrow, we can say that the individual has reached a high level of spiritual maturation. And conversely, if the area is great, then we conclude that his degree of spiritual maturation is scant. In instances where the therapist is unable to find any awareness of "ought" within his patient, no comparison is possible and he must therefore presume that the patient is virtually devoid of any significant spiritual development.

There are, however, other factors that must be considered before a definitive diagnosis of spiritual illness is made. One must make allowances for age, environmental factors, ethnic background, and religious and social heritage. All of these factors become pertinent when one is attempting to establish the diagnosis of spiritual illness.

We can therefore say that the primary basis upon which the diagnosis of spiritual illness is made is founded upon the triple analysis of the three component parts of this complex human malady. No attempt has been made to describe the various gradations or intensities of this syndrome. And telotherapy, like clinical psychology, finds it difficult to ascertain the precise moment when a state of acceptable developmental immaturity becomes an illness. Experience alone seems to provide the key to these evaluations. Softer terms like "spiritual deficiency" or "lack of spiritual growth" or "significant spiritual immaturity" are extremely useful when attempting to convey the nature of the illness to the patient.

Therapeutic Phase

The second major division in telotherapy is the therapeutic phase. Once spiritual illness has been diagnosed, treatment should begin. I have found it useful to separate in my thinking the theoretical aspects of treatment from the practical. In this way, I am constantly aware of what I am trying to achieve with therapy.

From a theoretical perspective, the treatment of spiritual illness utilizes two fundamental dynamic concepts: replacement and movement. Both of these processes go on simultaneously, but for the sake of discussion we will temporarily divide them each from the other.

The concept of replacement is forthright. The therapist hopes to replace those inadequate and unfulfilling features of the ailing patient with something more adequate and more fulfilling. Unlike much of contemporary psychiatry, telotherapy spends little time shoring up weak and porous defense mechanisms in order to protect an immature individual from the tensions and torments of life. Instead, its focuses upon developing a new being: one who will be inwardly strong and who will need little in the way of defense against the vicissitudes of life—except that which protects his opportunity to receive and give love. Telotherapy also wants to set people free to share their exuberance and joy for life with others. It wants to release these patients from the need to expend precious energy in the nonproductive efforts of personality defense and allow them to use it creatively to bring happiness and wholeness to others.

What are some of these features that need replacement? What does telotherapy have to offer in exchange? In place of hostility, telotherapy offers love, for guilt it offers forgiveness, for pain it gives comfort, for boredom it offers purpose, for sorrow it gives joy, for inner turmoil it offers peace, for loneliness it gives companionship, and in place of despair, telotherapy offers genuine hope.

The second therapeutic dynamic is movement, a movement toward unity and fulfillment. The therapist wants the patient to move his existential "is" toward closer union with his essential "ought."

In other words, he wishes to help the patient diminish his three-way estrangement from God, self, and others.

It should be recognized from the beginning that no patient, by himself, or even with the help of the most skillful therapist, can overcome this separation. Only the appropriate response to the love of God on the part of the patient will close this gap between the "ought" and the "is" and accomplish this healing phenomenon. But the telotherapist, who functions in many capacities—as analyst, counselor, educator, and friend—must above all else serve as the medium through which the love of God may be transmitted.

Love is such a frequent and dominant force in the dynamics of both replacement and movement that it would be advantageous to consider some of its various forms and functions.

It has often been said how unfortunate it is that the English language has virtually limited itself to the use of one word to describe the many kinds and manifestations of love: that which exists between individuals, between man and God, between God and man, as well as the love of other animate and inanimate objects. It also creates considerable confusion when psychologists and psychiatrists utilize the singular term love to describe the many levels of self-affection and interpersonal attractions. In the Greek language at least four words are used to distinguish one form of love from another: *agape, epithymia, eros* and *philia.*

Agape (a-*gap*-e) is the most difficult kind of love to understand, for it is of God and not of man. It differs from all forms of human love, yet it can be found to simulatneously participate in each of the various forms of human love. *Agape* is used throughout the Greek versions of the New Testament to express this unique form of love called "divine love" or "God's love." But it is also used on occasion to describe a special kind of love that exists between man and man and between man and God. We will attempt, with the help of Tillich, to delineate these various kinds of love that bind humans with humans and humans with God, and God with all of creation. And we will rely upon psychology to supply the information regarding the several forms of self-love.

Agape love, as we have said, is divine love. It both transcends and fulfills all forms of human love. What makes an understanding of *agape* so essential is the fact that no form of human love can ever find ultimate fulfillment apart from *agape*. When we say that man is "separated," he is in fact separated from this divine love of God. But *agape* provides both the power and the means for man to overcome his triple estrangement and provides both the hope and the possibility for fulfillment. *Agape* becomes the central healing force for all telotherapy. And telotherapy becomes the method by which *agape* love is transmitted to those who suffer from spiritual illness. *Agape* is introduced to those who suffer from spiritual illness by making them aware of their acceptance by God. Yet *agape* is not limited only to acceptance; it has other dimensions as well. *Agape* is also forgiving, transforming, healing, sacrificial, enduring, limitless, universal and in a total sense, incomprehensible. We begin to learn about these qualities only when we have passed through the phenomenon of acceptance. To know *agape* is to know God, for God is *agape*.

The other three words—*epithymia, philia,* and *eros*—are used to express the various kinds of human love: love between man and man and love between man and God. The first word, *epithymia,* means desire, but is better understood in its Latin form *libido*. *Libido,* says Tillich, is the movement of the needy toward that which fulfills the need. This term includes the dynamics of the sexual dimension of human love. Freud was intensely preoccupied with this one segment of human love. For him it represented the primary biological force in man that motivated him not only to gain pleasure, but to seek release from the unresolved tensions emanating from the *id.* Unfortunately, Freud did not grasp the full meaning of *libido,* because he failed to see that neither man's (nor woman's) sexual tensions nor biological needs are ever successfully relieved or fulfilled unless he or she is willing to accept the one who attempts to fulfill those needs. Unilateral *libido* is lust, and exploits the one who physically and emotionally fulfills the need. Mature *libido* fulfills both the giver and the recipient.

Tillich claims that love as *philia* is the movement of the equal toward union with the equal. This is the type of love seen in the friendships that exist between people with no reference or inference toward sexuality. *Philia* represents the friendship between men, between women, and between men and women that arise through mutual interests and ideas.

And love as *eros,* declares Tillich, is the movement of that which is lower in power and meaning to that which is higher. But *eros* is not limited to love alone. *Eros,* according to Plato, is a rational or cognitive force that drives the mind toward that which is ultimately true. Yet from a theological perspective, *eros* drives man both emotionally and intellectually toward God. It motivates man to move from where he is in his existential predicament toward that which will resolve it. Human *eros,* in its purest form, always pushes man toward God.

It should be noted that in each of these three forms of human love there is the unmistakable element of desire. In each case, the seeker wishes to unite with the one who bears or can fulfill that love. Yet all human love is affected by fluctuating human elements: attraction and repulsion, passion and dispassion, empathy and disdain. This is not true of *agape. Agape* accepts man "in spite of" his present or past behavior. There are no human contingencies necessary to make man acceptable to God. Man has only to accept the fact that he is acceptable precisely "as he is."

There is yet a fifth dimension of love that is called *Christian love.* Christian love is neither identical to *agape* nor to any of the various forms of human love. Christian love is fulfilled human love that arises out of a union between human and divine love. Many assume Christian love to be synonymous with *agape* and say that it is merely God's abstract love made concrete. But Christian love is the result of a unified response of all of the many forms of human love to *agape* as seen and exemplified in the person of Jesus the Christ. For a beautiful and matchless description this form of love, we have only to read Paul's thirteenth chapter of his First Letter to the Corinthians. Each of the five terms used offers a significant and qualifying expression of this ambiguous but frequently used term called love.

It is hoped that you will grasp some of the unique features of each of these various forms of love and see how each, and especially *agape*, plays such a vital role in applied telotherapy.

Applied Telotherapy

The methods of applying telotherapy are not meant to be rigid, yet some rather specific guidelines must be put forth in order to provide a framework for a systematic approach to this healing art. Later, as one gains sufficient experience in this fundamental approach, modifications can be used and superior adaptation of therapeutic techniques can be applied. But in the beginning, a step-by-step approach will offer most therapists a secure foundation for learning and applying telotherapy.

In general, telotherapy has three definite and sequential phases through which the afflicted person should be taken if optimal results are to be achieved. They are divided into preliminary, intermediate and advanced phases of therapy. Each phase has certain specific objectives that make it unique. Yet the dynamics of telotherapy are such that it is not necessary that every requirement of each phase be met before moving on to the next. Some patients' progress will allow them to circumvent certain facets of the therapeutic process. One should never lose sight of the fact that the principal purpose of telotherapy is to heal the spiritual illness and not to make a patient conform to any preconceived formula of therapy.

The Preliminary Phase of Telotherapy

The preliminary phase is synonomous with the analytical phase. Its chief purpose is to observe and evaluate the patient's symptoms, thoughts, and actions, and in so doing, to construct a complete and systematic analysis upon which a diagnosis of the nature of his illness can be made. One does not usually develop this analysis easily or quickly. Frequently, it is a slow and somewhat laborious procedure. People simply do not divulge their innermost thoughts to a stranger in the span of a few short hours. Initial meetings should be spent in developing rapport, trust, confidence, and mutual respect. They should also provide the patient with the opportunity to spill out many of his more superficial fears and frustrations as well as to ventilate some of his hostilities and anxieties. Early sessions are best used for unstructured patient catharsis. Later meetings are designed for more structured and systematic history-taking.

There are some important techniques and dynamics used in interviewing those who seek help for their emotional problems. Making an analysis is more than asking questions and recording answers. Let us focus upon four of the most essential and fundamental ingredients of all therapeutic counseling.

1. Listening and Observing   Listening to the individual who is seeking help provides the primary source of information necessary for the diagnosis of spiritual illness. Listening also offers the key to future therapy. It is not as easy as one would suppose. Too few therapists ever learn to listen to what the patient has to say. And too few therapists can resist the temptation to talk rather than listen. But because listening ultimately determines the mode and direction of treatment, it behooves all telotherapists to learn the art of careful listening. In *Principles of Intensive Psychotherapy,* Frieda Fromm-Reichmann states,

"The psychotherapist must be able to listen. This does not appear to be a startling statement, but it is intended to be just that. To be able to listen and to gather information from another person in this other person's own right, without reacting along the lines of one's own problems or experiences, of which one may be reminded, perhaps in a disturbing way, is an art of interpersonal exchange which few people are able to practice without special training."[13]

Hesse also describes this unique quality in his mystical book *Siddhartha.*

"It was one of the ferryman's greatest virtues that, like few people, he knew how to listen. Without his saying a word, the speaker felt that Vasudeva took in every word, quietly, expectantly, that he missed nothing. He did not await anything with impatience and gave neither priase nor blame—he only listened. Siddhartha felt how wonderful it was to have such a listener who could be absorbed in another person's life, his strivings, his sorrows.[14]

One also must observe the patient as he talks. The therapist must watch all facial, hand and, indeed, all bodily activity that accompanies the patient's verbal catharsis. He should observe all the inflections in his voice that might indicate the amount of emotional content or relative significance of what the patient is trying to reveal or hide. The presence or absence of tears or laughter, frowns or smiles, and if these expressions are in keeping with what the patient is actually saying should be observed. The patient's physical posture may also provide important information, such as how he sits or stands. Does he pace the floor or refuse to take the chair offered him? Does he smoke, drum his fingers on the arm of the chair, or play with some inanimate object? What are his facial expressions? Do his eyes meet yours or does he prefer to avoid all eye contact? How much hostility or apathy do you detect? How much kindness or frustration do you see? How much of the mask of depression does he wear? Are his expressions fixed or flexible? Does he look like he is telling you the truth about himself or is he telling what he thinks you want to hear? Can you see and feel his suffering? All these and more must be the observations of every astute and empathetic telotherapist.

2. *Accepting*   A second element is the dynamics of acceptance. The therapeutic benefits that accrue through a patient's verbal catharsis or from venting his inner feelings have long been recognized. The efficacy of catharsis is to be found in nearly every marriage and has formed the nucleus for much of the therapeutic dynamics of modern psychology and psychiatry. Surprisingly, the therapeutic benefits of catharsis do not arise primarily out of the patient's willingness to reveal his personal secrets or from the inward motivation to "get

things off his chest." The success or failure of any verbal release resides in the response of the listener. Several implicit as well as explicit requests are found in nearly all cases of genuine soul-venting. Most are cryptic but many are overt. Yet to the ears of the careful listener there are several very discernible pleas. Most are saying, "Listen to me, understand me, help me, accept me," and finally, "love me!" If the listener is indifferent, insensitive, or hostile, little or no relief will be gained. But if the listener is alert and compassionate and responds with love, kindness, and concern, the results will usually be beneficial.

The therapeutic dynamic of catharsis resides in the fact that the confessor has been accepted. Once the patient feels that he has been accepted precisely as he is, his anxiety diminishes. It is the unqualified, nonjudgmental acceptance of the one seeking help which provides both the foundation and atmosphere for all future therapy. For just as listening is imperative for diagnosis, acceptance provides the basis for nearly all effective telotherapy.

Acceptance of the patient includes several salient factors. First, the therapist must be willing to accept the patient not only as he is but also as an equal. This irrevocable and uncompromising fact of the equality of all men is theologically grounded and is explicit in the statement of faith regarding the essential nature of man. It is not an equality arising from a measurement of existential wisdom or skills or physical prowess. Nor is it an equality predicated upon an equal degree of social attainment. Rather, it is the equality originating in the gift of human creation. It might prove humbling for some to realize that God doesn't acclaim the therapist as being superior to the patient. If this were not so, how disadvantaged each of us would become when the role of therapist and patient changes, as it often does.

A second feature of acceptance, which is inextricably tied to the first, is the therapist's recognition that he, like his patient, is also unfulfilled and a fellow sufferer. Though the actual unfulfilling acts (sins) and mode of suffering may differ, the fact of relative separation from God that arises primarily through the perpetuation of self-will over God's will, will be recognized as a common and constant denominator within every patient and every telotherapist.

The third ingredient in the dynamics of acceptance is the awareness that accepting the patient as he is is merely a continuation and projection of the gift of acceptance that he, the therapist, has already received from God. Each telotherapist becomes God's surrogate and in a very real sense, a transmitter of *agape* love. Any therapist who has been accepted and forgiven by God will know what I mean. Jung provides still further insight into the dynamics of acceptance when he says, "The patient does not feel himself accepted unless the very worst in him is accepted too. . . . We cannot change anything unless we accept it. Condemnation does not liberate, it oppresses. I am the oppressor of the person I condemn, not his friend and fellow-sufferer.[15]

A fourth manifestation of acceptance is the expressed willingness on the part of the therapist to take on the patient for treatment. This acceptance comes after a period of serious introspection by the therapist to determine if he feels capable of offering significant assistance in ameliorating or modifying the patient's suffering. The therapist must answer this question before he agrees to accept the patient for therapy and to exert all reasonable effort to lead the patient toward spiritual health. If he answers in the affirmative, then all of the initial criteria for acceptance have been fulfilled.

3. Probing Probing is another essential ingredient in therapeutic counseling. It seeks to uncover the spiritual pathology responsible for the present illness. In order to glean this information, a moderately aggressive attitude is required. But too much aggressiveness will tend to threaten the patient, causing him to become defensive and thereby greatly diminishing the chance to gain helpful information through dialogue. However nondirective passivity will not produce the information needed for this analysis. Perhaps it is a balanced or kindly aggressiveness that is most needed at this point in our therapy.

4. Revealing the Analysis   The revelation of the dynamics of spiritual illness to the patient requires adroitness. It can be either constructive or destructive, therapeutic or detrimental. It can be presented with an air of remedial expectancy or put forth as an ominously hopeless condition that almost defies treatment. There are those therapists who will prefer to paint a black picture so that any progress will seem miraculous. Yet this philosophy, which protects the therapist, produces harmful anxiety in the patient and either intensifies his suffering or drives him to seek help elsewhere.

Some therapists will tend to present the dynamics of the illness in almost a professorial manner, which conveys an attitude of superiority. This presentation may bolster the ego of the therapist but does little to support the troubled and anxious patient. The therapist should explain the situation to the patient much as he would share a bit of information with a friend.

The question arises, how much should be disclosed to the patient? The obvious answer should be: no more than the therapist feels the patient is capable of accepting. Too much information in too short a period of time can prove to be overwhelming and threatening to the patient and could literally destroy any opportunity for beneficial assistance.

Another consideration is the use of terms that the patient can comprehend. Theological jargon is foreign to most people on anything but a very superficial plane, and much of their theological understanding is distorted and erroneous. But theological truths can be transmitted in simpler terms. The therapist must learn that teaching will always be a major part of his therapeutic process and he should constantly improve his ability to communicate.

Finally, the analysis always focuses on the fact of the patient's separation from God. And because primary separation is common to all mortals and does not in and of itself produce spiritual illness, the therapist moves toward the factors that have caused his secondary separation from God. No attempt is made at this juncture to suggest to the patient how this secondary estrangement might be overcome. Only the fact and the features of secondary separation are emphasized.

In sharp contrast to the therapeutic discipline of psychoanalysis, telotherapy sees only slight relief and comfort arising from the disclosure of the dynamics that participate in the patient's illness. Revealing the analysis in telotherapy only provides a foundation for future therapy by delineating the nature of the obstacles to be overcome. But seldom does the revelation of the nature and the magnitude of the problem offer much solace or therapeutic benefit other than the assurance to the patient that the therapist at least knows and cares about what is causing his suffering. The phenomenon of healing occurs primarily in the intermediate and advanced phases of telotherapy; only rarely is much relief obtained in this preliminary phase of treatment beyond the patient's feeling of being accepted.

Intermediate Phase of Telotherapy

Each phase of telotherapy becomes more demanding than the last, both to the therapist and to the patient. Because this is the last phase in which the therapist himself plays a dominant role and because this is the area of knowledge and expertise unique to those with a theological orientation, it will, without a doubt, prove to be the most challenging. This segment of therapy involves at least four divisions of emphasis. Each portion could and often does go on simultaneously, but like the preliminary phase, there is some definite advantage in adhering to a preconceived pattern. If it does nothing more than provide the therapist with a sense of security and the patient with a sense of planned progression, it will be of value. We will first present the components of this intermediate phase in outline form and will follow it with a more detailed discussion of each of the divisions.

Theological Education
    The nature of man
    The nature of God

Theological Education   Most people are theologically ignorant. Furthermore, they are ignorant of their ignorance. Religion for too many has been primarily, if not solely, an emotional experience practically devoid of any rational apprehension. It therefore seems only fair to assume that most people who will be seeking the assistance of a telotherapist will fall into this general category of the theologically uninformed. Not that these patients will have been lacking in church experience, nor will they be unfamiliar with religious terminology, like God, sin, faith, and evil. But categorically speaking, they will not have a very clear or mature concept of the central Christian doctrines. So the challenge of theological enlightenment will occupy the main portion of this initial phase of intermediate therapy.

Because of their unfamiliarity with and the abstract nature of theological thought, it will require great patience on the part of the therapist. Fortunately, however, the therapist will not, (and should not), be the only source of theological information for his patient. He may decide to use group therapy to expose many patients simultaneously to his theological teachings. He will also be helped by other ministers who disseminate theological truths through their teaching. There are also many classes in the Christian faith available in the framework of the organized church that provide not only theological knowledge, but a group environment with discussion and interaction to stimulate what could be a very dry and unimaginative experience in didactic learning.

Then, of course, there is the Bible. The Bible contains most, but certainly not all, of the valuable literature pertaining to man's understanding of God. But the Bible is not an easy collection of books to read, especially for the uninitiated and the uniformed. So to glibly tell a patient to read the Bible would be like telling a psychiatric patient to read a compendium of Sigmund Freud's work on neuropsychoses or a textbook on modern psychiatry. The patient must receive instruction on *how* to read the Bible if he is to get the greatest amount of knowledge and satisfaction. Now there are several more readable translations of the Bible that remove much of the ancient language barrier so prevalent in the King James version, the Vulgate, and other older translations. There are also many fine books and articles which will furnish the patient with additional insight to his relationship to God.

The therapist should also provide each patient with a list of books or articles with which he is personally acquainted rather than suggesting that the patient pick out anything that might appeal to him. Remember, these patients need help in a very specific rather than in a general way. For those who are just beginning their exposure to theological thought, any or all of the following would be useful: *Go Inquire of the Lord,* by Gerald Kennedy; *Making Religion Real* and *Strengthening Spiritual Life,* both by Nels Ferré; and *A Testament of Devotion,* by Thomas Kelly. These books are relatively simple in their language, but profoundly deep in their content. Two other introductory books that are slightly more academic are Gordon Allport, *The Individual and His Religion,* and John Magee, *Religion and Modern Man.* These next four books, *A New Being* and *The Shaking of the Foundations,* by Paul Tillich; *Deliverance to the Captives,* by Karl Barth; and *The Cost of Discipleship,* by Dietrich Bonhoeffer, would be very stimulating for the intermediate reader. And for those who wish to progress to an even higher level of theological thought, I recommend Paul Tillich, *Systematic Theology* (in three volumes); Reinhold Niebuhr, *The Nature and Destiny of Man;* and some of the works of Soren Kierkegaard. If the patient has already reached or surpassed this point in his reading, he will seldom need any further assistance from the therapist in his selection of books.

One satisfactory way for the therapist to begin his patient's education is to start with a simple discussion of the nature of man from a theological perspective.

THE NATURE OF MAN   A theological concept of man is essential to the whole notion of telotherapy and represents an integral part of treatment. Without it, telotherapy would make little sense either to the therapist or the patient. And because this method of apprehending man is so necessary to this healing discipline, it will be dealt with at greater lengths in a later chapter.

The patient must become aware that theology expands the understanding of man beyond the usual perimeters defined by scientific evaluation or from the collective points of view given us by the behavioral sciences. He should be encouraged to see that from a theological perspective there are three phases to man's total life: creation, existential and eternal life. Moreover, the therapist should convey the Christian belief that man enters the existential phase of life in a state of separation and unfulfillment. Man is separated from God. It should be explained further that the purpose of existential life is to overcome this estrangement and reunite with God. Reunion is man's fulfillment.

Outler succinctly places man in proper theological perspective when he says, "Man is neither alone nor supreme in his universe. The universe is not indifferent to his fate. He is not his own final reliance. He is, first and last, God's creature, endowed with freedom-in-finiteness."[16]

THE NATURE OF GOD   Where does one begin to explain the Ultimate Reality we call God? Words alone seem not to be the primary means by which God becomes real to another person. The use of such traditional theological terms as Omnipotent, Omnipresent, and Omniscient are just too archaic to be relevant, even when their meaning is properly explained. Or, to recite yet another beautiful triad—that God is Creator, Sustainer, and Redeemer—seems equally ineffective in today's world for communicating the likeness of God. So how can one convey the nature of God to another human, especially one who is in the throes of suffering from the agonies of his spiritual illness? Most often I have found it best to help the patient "feel" the presence of God, rather than to intellectualize any concept of a Supreme Being. And I believe it is true for nearly all of us that the reality of God is experienced only when we feel his presence.

It has taken me a long time to realize the wisdom of Tillich's statement that faith preceeds belief. I had thought the reverse was true, but not so. Faith, in a theological sense, is not belief in doctrine; it is being grasped by the Ultimate Reality, which is God. In other words, God is felt before he is understood. Belief follows faith, and is the intellectual response to the experience of faith. So each therapist must assist his patient to feel the presence of God in order to begin the healing process. Again, how is this accomplished? How does one help another experience God? There is, of course, no precise or complete answer to this question. Nevertheless, there is a partial answer that merits our consideration. We can rightfully assume that any patient is most likely to experience God in an atmosphere of love and in a time of need than under nearly any other circumstance. So the therapist begins by showing the patient the likeness of God by loving him, expressing this by the act of acceptance. Acceptance, therefore, becomes a combined manifestation of human and divine love, or Christian love, and it is through this medium that the patient is most likely to experience the reality of God.

In order to develop our theory of progressive telotherapy, we will assume that the patient has become aware of his acceptance by God, either directly or vicariously through the therapist. Hopefully, the joy that accompanies the recognition of acceptance by God will motivate the patient to take the next critical step in the process of healing; namely, the acceptance of God. Up to this point, the patient has been a passive recipient of treatment, and little or nothing has been required of him. But all subsequent steps in the healing process requires the patient's most active participation. An acceptance of God includes: an awareness of responsibility and guilt, obtaining God's forgiveness, and making a commitment to God. These chronological steps show how the patient may develop his acceptance of God.

Because the dynamics of guilt and forgiveness play such an important role in nearly every case of spiritual illness, perhaps we should digress and consider some of the theoretical therapeutic dynamics that telotherapy has to offer in the way of eradicating the destructive forces of guilt through forgiveness.

The need for forgiveness arises from an awareness of guilt. And guilt has its origin in an awareness of responsibility. Feeling guilty makes us painfully uncomfortable, and an act of forgiveness, so we believe, will eliminate our suffering. But "feeling guilty" and "being guilty" are two different things. One can feel guilty without being guilty and one can be guilty without feeling guilty. Unfortunately, the world seems to be filled with too many people who should feel guilty but who do not, and with a substantial number of those who feel guilty but who should not. Being guilty is a judgment that is placed upon an individual either by himself, by society, or by God. Feeling guilty is quite another matter. It can arise out of assumed guilt rather than actual guilt and therefore may not always be justified. However, assumed guilt can and does produce the same kind and degree of suffering as does actual guilt, and for the remainder of this discussion they will be considered as though they were the same.

Guilt feelings, from a psychological standpoint, usually result when the individual fails to meet a preset standard of personal conduct or thought. This inner judgmental mechanism is commonly referred to as one's superego or conscience. This superego or conscience is usually influenced by as many extrinsic as intrinsic factors. It is tempered and molded by forces within the individual's environment: parents, family, associates, education, the prevailing moral and legal laws, and in many instances by religious convictions. People who feel that God has a claim upon their lives are more prone to experience guilt than those who do not believe this. Guilt, from a more panoramic and theological perspective, is assumed to grow out of unfulfilled or ruptured relationships between the individual and himself, between the individual and others, and between the individual and God. Most people are best acquainted with the first two categories and only a relatively few with the latter. However, anything that separates us from ourselves or from others also separates us from God. The reverse is even more frequently true, but less frequently recognized.

In his hypothesis about the dynamics of the development of the human mental structure, Freud describes guilt as one of the many forms of anxiety that arise from conscious or unconscious conflict between the id, ego and superego. He describes the superego as the special portion of the ego that contains the individual's censorship mechanism, which decides what is right or wrong, good or evil, acceptable or unacceptable. When the individual does something which runs contrary to his sense of rightness, goodness, or acceptability, a condition of painful unrest is created due to the lack of harmony between these three interrelated mental mechanisms. This emotional response, he says, is a feeling of guilt.[17]

He goes on in a subsequent paper, *The Defense in Neuropsychoses*, to elaborate the many ways in which man attempts to protect himself from experiencing the pain of guilt and other forms of anxiety. Most of these defense mechanisms operate, says Freud, on an unconscious level. It is not necessary to mention all of them, but the ones which are most frequently used and are most readily recognized are the mechanisms of denial, repression, rationalization, projection, and sublimation. Variations of these are used daily to prevent or assuage feelings of guilt and anxiety.

It was Freud's conclusion that guilt could be dealt with in at least three ways: first, to modify one's superego by making it more flexible and less demanding; second, to utilize the ego defense mechanisms in an optimally efficient manner; and third, to allow an appropriate form of punishment to "neutralize" the feeling of guilt. At no time, however, does Freud include the concept of responsibility as an integral factor in the production of guilt feelings. Nor does he ever mention the possibility that forgiveness might be the remedy for guilt.

This is but one of the many areas in which telotherapy differs from psychotherapy. It seems to me that modern psychiatry offers no definitive solution for the dilemma of human guilt, for neither punishment, modification of the superego, nor any form of denial, repression, or rationalization will ever eradicate guilt. While it may temporarily diminish it, it never removes it. Forgiveness alone provides the only permanent resolution for guilt.

Too often in a therapeutic situation our attention focuses in on the dynamics of a particular guilt feeling that we think holds the key to the patient's suffering. But we must never lose sight of the fact that the basic guilt that supersedes and underlies all others is the willful separation of the individual from God. Until this estrangement is overcome, the patient will be unable to rectify any other feelings of guilt.

There are four different varieties of forgiveness: God's forgiveness, self-forgiveness, forgiveness of others, and forgiveness by others. Each plays a unique role in alleviating feelings of guilt and releasing the individual from one of the many forms of emotional incapacity.

The process of obtaining God's forgiveness is the most essential of all of the various forms of forgiveness. God's forgiveness determines, to a very large extent, the individual's ability to forgive himself and others; it therefore becomes a major force in the total healing process.

The second step is self-forgiveness. Unless we can forgive ourselves, our guilt persists. Sequentially, self-forgiveness follows the acceptance of God's forgiveness. This fact is seldom appreciated or even recognized. Most of us seek self-forgiveness long before we even contemplate the possibility of needing God's forgiveness. We try nearly every means of self-deception and self-encouragement, and offer ourselves multiple excuses in a vain attempt to forgive ourselves. But eventually we discover we have neither the power nor the authority to forgive ourselves. Without God's pardon, self-pardon is impossible. This is understood only when we review our theological concept of man as well as expand our understanding of the dynamics of guilt.

Personal guilt arises when we either do or do not do something we know we ought to do or not do. Personal guilt is generated when we fall short of being what we know we ought to be. This "ought to be" is the spiritual counterpart to Freud's superego. This "ought" is the human-divine potential that we seek to make real and that is our inner goal or *telos*. Therefore, anything we do or don't do that runs contrary to our inner goal creates feelings of guilt. So our guilt should arise not so much from letting ourselves down, but from letting God down. It is to him that we must feel our ultimate responsibility.

A frequent sufferer is the so-called perfectionist. He has set for himself extremely high, rigid, and on close scrutiny, unrealistic standards for his personal performance. He exudes self-confidence, self-discipline, and self-righteousness—until he makes a major mistake. At that moment, he becomes utterly deflated and his suffering is of unbelievable intensity. His self-punishment is unrelenting and unmerciful, and usually extends far beyond the magnitude of his error. He has structured a life situation in which there is no room for pardon, including his own. To alter his standards would be tantamount to a second defeat as unacceptable as his error, which produced his initial feeling of guilt. Oddly enough, the basic defect in every perfectionist is not his unreasonable high and inflexible standard for personal striving. Rather, it resides in the fact that he has designed his life to please himself and to gain recognition of others, instead of living to please God and accepting himself as an imperfect creature worthy of forgiveness within the framework of God's grace.

Forgiveness of others is the third sequential step in the cycle of forgiveness. The importance of this dimension of forgiveness was repeatedly stressed by Jesus. One of the most familiar references is to be found in the Sermon on the Mount as recorded in the book of Matthew. The first reference is in the Lord's Prayer:

Forgive us the wrong we have done,
As we have forgiven those who have wronged us.

For if you forgive others the wrongs they have done,
Your heavenly Father will also forgive you;
But if you do not forgive others,
Then the wrongs you have done will not be forgiven by your Father.[18]

Much confusion has arisen from this passage. If taken literally, we would conclude that Jesus meant that God's forgiveness is absolutely dependent upon man's willingness to forgive others who have offended him. It furthermore implies that if man is unwilling to forgive others, God would retaliate by refusing to forgive man. I believe that much of the seeming harshness and punitive quality of this imperative could be eliminated if we would review the situation under which Jesus issued these words. He was talking primarily to his own twelve disciples, who had undoubtedly on many previous occasions experienced the forgiving grace of God. They were not mere novices in their understanding of the terms of Christian discipleship, nor were they neophytes in experiencing God's healing power. They knew, at least in part, what God requires of those who would follow him. And God always demands more from the more mature Christians than from the newly initiated. Therefore, Jesus was telling his more mature followers that if they expected to continue to receive God's forgiveness, they must be willing to forgive those who have wronged them.

But I am firmly convinced that this rule does not apply equally to the novice who has not yet experienced the forgiving love of God. For it is only after each of us has experienced the forgiveness of God that we learn to forgive others who have offended us. The sequence, therefore, is initially God's forgiveness, self-forgiveness, and then the forgiveness of others. It is only as we grow in our understanding of these dynamics that we can more fully comprehend the teachings of Jesus and avoid the pitfalls that literal interpretations often create. Yet for the mature Christian, Jesus' imperative stands. God indeed expects man to forgive others not only so that he can receive forgiveness for himself, but so that Christians will lighten the load and diminish the guilt of those around them. God wishes to make his love felt throughout the entire human community.

Forgiveness by others must also be mentioned. It is really a special category of forgiveness, for it lies almost completely outside the realm of the individual's control and in a manner that differs from one's interpersonal relationship with God. We cannot make anyone forgive us. Ultimately, it is contingent upon the offended individual's willingness to accept our apology and grant us his pardon. But there are several factors that help to create a climate conducive for eliciting forgiveness from one whom we have offended. Not least of these is an attitude of true contrition combined with a frank admission of guilt. Obviously, an admission of fault and the expressed desire for forgiveness should not be carried to the point of absurdity to include endless penance, self-flagellation, and unrelenting remorse. All that is required is a genuine acknowledgement of guilt, a spirit of contrition, and the hope of forgiveness.

The joy that accompanies an act of human forgiveness is second only to the ecstacy experienced when one is forgiven by God. In reality, however, human forgiveness is merely an extension of God's forgiveness. This joy is inexplicable and only partial descriptions are possible. It is like having a heavy weight lifted from one's shoulders, being released from prison, or like stepping out of darkness into light. Human forgiveness provides the chance to reestablish a relationship that had been broken and paves the way for making it even better than before.

Conversely, the sadness, frustration, and inner anguish that prevails when one human being refuses to forgive another is incalculable. It generates an antisocial and destructive atmosphere. Yet, despite the fact that some people will never forgive one who has offended them, there is a compensatory mechanism that circumvents the need for any human forgiveness. God's forgiveness and self-forgiveness can and does adequately remove all guilt in spite of the absence of human forgiveness. God's forgiving love never succumbs to human stubbornness.

The telotherapist can offer one additional element of encouragement to his patient: the relentless nature of God's pursuit of man. Most depressed patients feel that if the hope for their cure must come solely from their own initiative, they are lost from the beginning. The very nature of despair is to be unable to see even a glimmer of hope, especially from within. Therapeutic Christianity says that man does not have to provide the initiative for his own recovery, but only a willingness to respond to God's invitation to healing. God is always the initiator; man is always the responder. We delude ourselves if we think the opposite is true, for even our reaching and crying out is in response to what we already know is there.

Dynamics of Prayer   Every serious prayer contains power, not because of the intensity of desire expressed in it, but because of the faith the person has in God's directing activity—a faith which transforms the existential situation.[19]— PAUL TILLICH

Telotherapy cannot function without prayer. Prayer is the means by which man communicates with God and God provides the means for healing. Prayer is also as essential to the therapist as it is to the patient. Both must be in working harmony with God or the possibility for amelioration of spiritual suffering is greatly reduced. Further, we must constantly remind ourselves that all healing is of God. Man may administer treatment, but he does not heal.

There are many excellent books for those seeking knowledge about prayer. I heartily recommend *Reality and Prayer,* by John Magee; *Prayer,* by George Buttrick; and the chapter on prayer in Nels Ferré's *Making Religion Real.* Each author has a slightly different slant on the dynamics of prayer that makes the reading of all three an enriching experience. There are also many fine books of prayers. Among many of exceptional quality are: *A Diary of Private Prayers,* by

John Baillie; *Lift Up Your Hearts,* by Russell Bowie; and *Are You Running With Me, Jesus?* and *Free to Live, Free to Die,* both by Malcolm Boyd.

Prayer is and most likely always will remain a mystery. It is mysterious because it is more than mere autosuggestion and certain words, a frame of mind, or a learned technique. The prayer of a humble man who says, "God, this is John" is as effective as a hundred "Hail Marys" or the continual recitation of the Lord's Prayer that places the precise amount of emphasis on each syllable of every word. Legend tells us that Moses once heard a shepherd praying, "O God, show me where thou art, that I may become Thy servant, I will clean Thy shoes, and comb Thy hair, and sew Thy clothes, and fetch Thee milk." Moses rebuked him: "God is a Spirit, and needs not such gross ministrations." Thereupon, the shepherd rent his clothes in dismay and fled to the desert. Then Moses heard a voice from Heaven, "O Moses, wherefore have you driven away my servant? . . . I regard not the words that are spoken, but the heart that offers them."[20]

Prayer has been defined as a "timed exposure of the soul to God." Or, to use a medical metaphor, prayer is the oxygen essential to sustain spiritual life. But it is still more. Prayer is the channel through which we establish our dynamic relationship with God. It is the best way we get to know the Mysterium Tremendum (Rudolf Otto). Prayer is man's means of gaining his acceptance and forgiveness from God. It is also the avenue by which he continues to receive the manifold forms of God's grace in the form of joy, strength, courage, mercy, comfort, and healing. Prayer also allows us to utilize these expressions of God's love not only for ourselves, but with others as well. Prayer makes it possible for us to recognize, accept, and transmit the love of God—which is the primary purpose of life. Without prayer, man can never develop his human-divine potential, for the maturation of his soul as well as the full development of his human talents requires God's assistance. Man is a God-dependent creature. Without prayer, guilt could never be removed for forgiveness becomes impossible. Acceptance, or the awareness of being loved by God, is a phenomenon that becomes a personal reality most often when we relate to God through prayer. Spiritual healing, too, becomes possible only through a meaningful relationship with God—which is accomplished primarily through prayer. Prayer is an indispensible ingredient in the dynamics of most, if not all, human-divine encounters. Prayer is the *sine qua non.*

Prayers are of many varieties. Some are spoken, many unspoken. Some are prayers of thankfulness and adoration. Others are prayers of petition and intercession. Prayers may also be a personal confession in which we ask God's forgiveness for unfulfilling acts of omission and commission. Or prayers may be merely a period of being in the presence of God, a moment of indescribable ecstacy.

Prayer is meant to be a two-way experience. Too often we become so busy making requests and emoting our inner feelings that we forget that God might have something worthwhile to say in return. There are those, however, who participate in prayer only to ask God for something. But God seldom gives us what we ask. This would presume that we always know what is best for us. We should learn from Jesus that the most mature way to end all prayers is with, "Yet not as I will, but as thou wilt."[21]

I have never actually heard God's audible voice as claimed by the prophets of old and by some very devout contemporary Christians. But this does not mean that I doubt that God speaks directly to individuals. I believe that God speaks to us most often through an "inner voice," much as we say our conscience speaks to us. And those who are in tune with God "hear" what He has to say.

The Therapeutic Role of the Church   The church plays a unique and often therapeutic role in our human society. No other institution in either ancient or modern times provides that which is offered by the church. There are three distinct, interrelated areas of group involvement in nearly every dynamic Christian church: corporate worship, fellowship, and service. Each will be discussed independently but you should keep in mind the interrelatedness and cohesiveness of these arbitrary divisions. Furthermore, a general and intrinsic similarity between the Catholic and Protestant branches of the Christian church is assumed, and no effort is made to point out the multitudinous minor and the few major differences that do exist.

CORPORATE WORSHIP Corporate worship is the act of worshiping God with a body of people having similar religious beliefs. The service, or liturgy, contains many different integrated items. It may include reading from the Bible, confessions, communion or eucharist, sermons, responsive readings, vocal and instrumental music, and so forth. This act of combined worship is usually held in a specially designed building containing varying numbers of religious symbols and with specifically designated locations for those participating in the various acts of worship. This structure is often erroneously called "the church" when, in fact, it is merely a building in which worshipers temporarily gather. The act of worship also includes periods of meditation, adoration, thanksgiving, confession, asking forgiveness, and learning theological truths that have past, present, and future application to existential living. This liturgy utilizes different forms and modes of expression that will vary not only from church to church, but from service to service within the same congregation. Yet the purpose of all worship services is to create an atmosphere conducive to reciprocal communication between man and God. Corporate worship represents a definite and concerted effort to create a milieu in which man may become personally aware of the presence of God and voluntarily accept his gifts of acceptance, forgiveness, and healing.

One could divide the service of worship into its more active and passive aspects, those areas that require greater or lesser degrees of individual participation. However, this would be only of academic interest. In reality, every phase, including listening, requires a certain amount of activity on the part of the supplicant. If an individual wishes to obtain the maximum benefit from the act of common worship, it will require considerable involvement on his part. Total passivity in worship seldom evokes a healing phenomenon. But even here we have an apparent contradiction. For no matter how analytical one becomes in dissecting the parts of a worship service and no matter how carefully he weighs the act of personal participation, the individual seems always to receive more than he invests and gets more than he deserves. This is both the mystery and the wonder of corporate worship.

CHRISTIAN FELLOWSHIP   A second therapeutic feature of the church is to be found within its Christian fellowship. This term has been used so promiscuously that it no longer has much of its original meaning or therapeutic implication. In spite of its almost flippant and pedestrian use, Christian fellowship, in its true form, still represents a unique type of interpersonal relationship that is unequaled in any other segment of the human society. It can perhaps be best thought of as the spontaneous exchange of human and *agape* love between those who earnestly seek to do the will of God. It also provides sustaining strength for all those who are members of the Christian community.

But Christian fellowship is more than this. It is a totally unselfish way of life. Its members accept the fact that they are their "brothers' keeper" and expand their area of responsibility to include those who reside outside of the fellowship as well. Furthermore, the members of the fellowship suffer vicariously for all humans who have not yet established a proper relationship with God. Christian fellowship expresses a concern not only for the spiritual health of the individual but for his mental, physical, and economic health as well. It actively assists those who are suffering from spiritual illness and eagerly hopes that they too will join the Christian community. But membership into this elite corps demands that each person relinquish his self-centered concept of life in exchange for a God-centered one.

A frequently missed therapeutic benefit of Christian fellowship is the fact that the patient soon realizes that each member has been down a road of despair similar to his own. His misery begins to diminish when he recognizes that he alone has not been singled out to suffer, and that there is genuine hope for his healing as verified by the healthy members within the Christian community. And as his exposure to these "joyful people" increases, he begins to catch a glimpse of the wisdom expressed by Nels Ferré when he said that few people ever find God except through suffering.

CHRISTIAN SERVICE   The third therapeutic aspect of the church is to be found in its Christian service. A church without action soon shrivels up and dies of attrition. But a church that actively becomes engaged in making life more meaningful and pleasant for others will continue to grow and flourish. Yet if the Christian service within the church is to achieve its highest level of effectiveness, it must establish a level of priorities and some reasonable concepts of definitive goals. Churches that have tried to respond to every demand have fallen far short of their expectations. But a church that has adopted an appropriate priority system, one which reflects its primary mission, usually sees more concrete results arising from its efforts.

A realistic schedule for Christian service should include these imperatives: helping those within its own membership, assisting those who seek help but who are not yet members, and reaching out into the local community, the nation, and finally into the world. On the surface of things, this priority system would seem to be inverted, self-centered, and contrary to the common Christian concept that places its emphasis on serving others first. But upon closer scrutiny, we will see that this is not necessarily the case. A church's self-service involves helping the members of the church to grow spiritually, to broaden their understanding and their dynamic relationship with God, and to assist the members to rid themselves of their hostility toward others and themselves. And it is only when the membership, both individually and collectively, becomes spiritually mature that it can make a significant therapeutic impact upon the community it wishes to serve.

Admittedly, a church that feeds only its own flock will never reach the apogee of Christian development. Therefore, after a reasonable degree of Christian maturation has been attained within a congregation, it must be willing to assist those outside of its own immediate membership. But there is a good reason for emphasizing the sequential development of Christian service in which a significant level of self-maturation precedes serving others. Many clinicians have observed that unless the therapist is stronger than his client, both may drown in the common sea of despair. The same is also true for the neophyte Christian who attempts to save a sinking soul when he himself has just barely learned to float.

Finally, the mark of a church that has truly reached maturity is one that fulfills the needs of its members, continues to assist nonmembers within its own community, and yet still has enough spiritual energy to reach out into the world to help those who have deprived themselves of God's love. Any person who affiliates himself with such a church will be grasped by the contagious spirit of *agape* love. It is this type of church that will support those who suffer from spiritual illness and give substantial aid to the telotherapist.

It has long been recognized that both direct and indirect benefits accrue to those patients who get involved in helping others. This same therapeutic phenomenon is frequently observed in patients who participate in nearly all forms of genuine Christian fellowship and service. Gordon Allport, the late social psychologist, relates an example of mentally ill patients receiving personal improvement as the result of assisting other mentally ill patients.

A certain psychiatrist requires the patients in his private sanitarium to attend and companion those and who are more ill than they. Such activity, he finds, has a markedly integrative effect, redeploying and re-centering the energies that were harmfully spent in self-pity, in resentment, in fantasy. The fact that health flows from the practice of the Christian virtue of charity is of no particular concern to this psychiatrist. To him the practice of charity is just one constructive interest capable of knitting together the broken personalities of his patients. The religionist, however, would maintain that the gain is far from accidental. Love—incomparably the greatest psychotherapeutic agent—is something that professional psychiatry cannot of itself create, focus nor release.[22]

Improvement within the individual who loves and serves others is not coincidental. It only validates one of the many laws of love that says, "It is in giving that we receive."

Unfortunately, too few churches provide the kind of totally integrated therapeutic program described here. Many may be strong in corporate worship but weak in Christian fellowship and service. Others may emphasize Christian service but provide virtually no Christian fellowship for its members. And altogether too many churches are preoccupied with the twin efforts of fund-raising and membership procurement and they spend little time or effort in developing their spiritual lives. So it is simply not enough for the telotherapist to tell his patients to go to church. He must be in a position to recommend a church whose priorities and development coincide with the patient's needs.

Waiting   There is a point in telotherapy when both the therapist and the patient must wait for God to break through and administer his healing power. Waiting makes us cognizant that God determines when man is ready to receive his gift of healing, reemphasizing the dependent nature of man. Remember that telotherapy, of itself, does not heal. Its principle function is to prepare the individual for receiving God's healing grace. Once prepared, the patient must wait. As Paul puts it, "Having done all, to stand."[23]

But whereas waiting humbles some, it anger others. Waiting for many patients is not a period for quiet inner reflection and hopeful anticipation. It is interpreted as merely another form of suffering to be added to what they already bear. In their impatience and smoldering hostility, some begin to demand healing from God with a threat implied. Others, less belligerent, will attempt devious ways to secure God's gift of healing with promises of tithing, regular church attendance, or by neurotically involving themselves in some kind of service for others. But all these attempts fail and we soon learn that we can never force, coerce, or cajole God into healing us. God never acquiesces to man's demands or ultimatums. The awful truth is that God alone decides when the right time is to bestow his redemptive and reconstructive love upon us. Man can only wait.

But rarely does God keep man waiting unless there is a reason.

Prolonged periods of waiting on the part of the patient usually suggests that the individual has not yet adequately relinquished his grasp upon his pride. I am convinced that God never permanently withholds his healing love from anyone who accepts his love and seeks his forgiveness. In every case where there is an interval of excessive delay between the patient's act of acceptance of God and his receiving the miracle of healing, we must again resume our search for some major impediment that prevents this therapeutic human-divine bond from developing.

Advanced Phase of Telotherapy

The advanced phase of telotherapy begins at the moment the patient feels he has experienced the unequivocal joy of healing and the release from his suffering. The waiting is over and his spiritual health has become a reality. The patient is aware that he has established a vital and meaningful relationship with God. He is a "new being" and now participates in a new dimension of reality. The patient has, in fact, grasped a large measure of his *telos*, caught a significant glimpse of what is meant by fulfillment, and is now ready to participate in the abundant life.

Dr. David Roberts describes the phenomenon of spiritual healing in this manner. He says,

Our defensive structures are broken through by healing power which is wider than ourselves; yet it is ours. We see—not merely intellectually, but with heart and soul—that what is made accessible to us in our "new" selves has been what we have yearned for all along. We have evaded it partly because the price in suffering seems too high, especially when there was no guarantee of a satisfying outcome. We have also "evaded" it because we literally could not work toward it effectively so long as we were imprisoned within the old strategies of defensiveness, anxiety and the need to feel superior.[24]

Sam Keen offers another exuberant expression of the moment of healing by describing it in terms of the individual's return from his exile of unreality. He says, "The haze in the air evaporates and world comes into focus; seeking gives way to finding; anxiety to satisfaction. Nothing is changed and everything is changed. Human existence ceases to be a problem to be solved and becomes a mystery to be enjoyed."[25] Healing is expressed in a cry of joy.

In this advanced phase of telotherapy, the patient ceases to feel any need for his therapist's skills and usually breaks all formal contact with him. This severance is the normal sequential development of every successful therapeutic situation. And this separation, like all others, has its unhappy side as well. In many instances, this dissolution of the patient-therapist relationship produces a temporary feeling of depression within the therapist, for the therapist has lost a love-object at the same time his patient has gained One. This transitory suffering on the part of the therapist is not unlike that felt by the parents of the bride and groom at nearly every wedding when they realize that their relationship with their child will never again be quite the same. Fortunately, this severance sorrow is usually short-lived, for the therapist quickly focuses his attention toward the next patient that enters his office.

There is, however, an explicit obligation that every patient of telotherapy assumes from the instant of his own healing—the obligation to share the gift of God's love with others through commitment. It is this continuum of the transmission of *agape* that provides hope for others who suffer from the pain and despair of their spiritual illness. This must be one of the conditions of treatment, for certainly there will never be enough telotherapists to do the job that needs to be done. Each healed patient should, out of his new abundant joy, become an emissary for God's healing love and pledge to participate in the abundant life.

There are numerous other ways in which telotherapy can be applied. What we have done is merely offered one of the many possible systematic methods of applying the healing power of God. But telotherapy can also be applied in a random manner and in differing ratios other than one therapist to one patient. It can be applied in large groups and small groups, homogeneous and heterogeneous groups. Yet it is a dedication to results rather than to methods that

I wish to emphasize most strongly. Fortunately, telotherapy is intrinsically flexible and can be applied in many different ways. So instead of becoming firmly attached to one method of treatment, we must explore all of the various possible methods of applying this healing potential in order to be able to offer maximum benefit to all those who suffer from this *dis*-ease of the spirit.

A special adaptation of telotherapy should be mentioned. For the want of a better name it can be referred to as concomitant therapy. Basically, it is a mode of treatment in which the patient assists others while he himself is receiving help. I am sure that it uses some of the same dynamic principles that the psychiatrist was applying to his patients in Dr. Roberts's illustration. It can be explained most simply in this fashion. The therapist outlines for the patient his full course of therapy. He says, in essence, "When you first come to me, I will love and accept you. When you begin to feel secure in my love, then you must go out and love someone who will respond to your love, and then return to me in order that you might receive more of my love. Next, you must go out and love someone who will welcome you, but who will not know how to receive your love, and then return again to me and I will love you. Finally, you must go out and love someone who needs your love, but who will be unwilling to accept it. When you can do this, and remain strong, you will no longer need to return to me, for you will have been healed."

In *Call to Commitment*, Elizabeth O'Connor gives an excellent example of a variation of this concomitant therapy in a church setting. The book itself is a testimony to the success of the application of this mode of therapy in a group or corporate situation.

In conclusion, telotherapy, no matter through what mode of application, deals with the diagnosis and treatment of spiritual illness. In every case, the phenomenon of healing results when the patient has achieved or regained his proper relationship with God through the dual miracles of acceptance and forgiveness, which are themselves expressions of God's love. But the process of healing begins on an existential rather than an ethereal level. It begins with the telotherapist accepting and loving the patient who comes seeking his assistance. Once the patient feels accepted and loved by his therapist, he begins to catch a glimpse of the purer form of God's love, which transcends and augments that which he has already received. And as he reaches beyond the therapist, he lets the mystery of God grasp him. Finally, healing is consummated when the patient accepts the love of God. He has become reunited and made whole. Telotherapy, therefore, is a process of administering *agape* and human love and directing the patient toward the primary source of all love in order that he might find health and fulfillment.

4
Mental or Spiritual Illness?

The interrelatedness between mental and spiritual illness and their respective modes of treatment can perhaps be best understood through the medium of mental imagery and the application of the dynamics of human depression. Envision a three-dimensional concept of an atom (or what we had thought until recently was the structure of an atom) with a centrally placed nucleus representing the psychologist's concept of self, containing its triad of id, ego, and superego, and the various circumferential electronic rings or shells denoting the individual's external environment. These electrons, or elements of the external environment, would represent all other human beings, especially those people who most frequently or significantly exert an influence upon the self as contained within the nucleus, e.g., family, teachers, friends, enemies, spouse, employer, etc., as well as all other physical and inanimate things. And, if one could further extend his power of imagination to penetrate this self-nucleus, he would notice that deeply embedded in the very center of self is man's spiritual component, which we call God. This introduces into our imaginary model a theological dimension.

Next, one must be able to perceive the constant dynamic interaction between the forces emanating from the nuclear portion of this atom with those from the encircling electrons or external environment. When we adapt this hypothetical concept to a therapeutic situation, the task of the therapist becomes one of determining what effect these various dynamic forces have evoked upon or within the suffering individual, which have been beneficial and which have been detrimental to his emotional health. Hopefully, this method of analysis would provide the necessary information for both the diagnosis and treatment of his emotional malady.

From this simple illustration it can be seen that the telotherapist would focus his attention primarily toward the center of man, where the interaction between self and God is most evident; whereas the psychologists and psychiatrists would direct their primary efforts toward the more peripheral aspects, where the dynamic interplay between self (minus a conscious awareness of God) and the significant elements in the external environment are most apparent. The term "primary" indicates only where the major emphasis of both therapeutic disciplines is placed. But it is imperative that the teleotherapist and the psychotherapist become aware not only of their juxtaposition but also of the many overlapping areas that their respective therapies will affect. In a very real sense, man with his many component parts is quite indivisible, except on a theoretical basis, and all attempts to divide him will prove futile.

We shall forget this conjectural metaphor for a moment and go on to the nature of depression.

Types of Depression

According to current psychiatric nomenclature, the emotional disease complex called depression is divided into two general categories: neurotic and psychotic. The line of demarcation between them is determined by the patient's degree of awareness of reality. If the patient is alert, rational, and obviously in contact with his environment, his depression is deemed to be of a neurotic nature. If, however, he is experiencing either auditory or visual hallucinations, or if his thought and behavioral patterns appear inappropriate and irrational, his malady is considered psychotic.

Additional diagnostic categories for depression have also been devised. Many psychiatrists believe there are basically two types of neurotic depression: reactive and endogenous. The reactive depression results from significant events within the individual's external environment that are responsible for his depression; for example, the loss of love objects through death or separation, the loss of a job or financial security, loss of health with the inability to enjoy life, or the lack of fulfillment of many hopes. The dynamics of endogenous depression are a bit vague and obscure. No apparent external forces seem to contribute as major etiologic factors in this form of depression. For many therapists, endogenous depression becomes a diagnosis by exclusion.

Some investigators, however, have suggested that a common cause for this form of depression is endocrine imbalance. By observing the frequency with which women experience depression during various phases of the menstrual cycle, during pregnancy, and throughout the span of menopause we can find substantial validation for this position. Furthermore, clinicians often see depression as the presenting symptom in certain other cases of hormonal imbalance, such as with hypo- and hyperthyroidism and in instances of tumor invasion of the pancreas and adrenal glands. Endogenous depression is also thought to be genetically transmitted. It is not uncommon to find several generations in the same family who have suffered from what appears to have been similar forms of depression. And if we were to apply this same method of classification to all forms of emotional response, it would seem logical to place spiritual illness in this general category of endogenous depression. It has both the spacial and dynamic qualifications and its primary activities are intranuclear. Yet spiritual illness, along with all other forms of endogenous depression, is affected by external as well as internal factors, so there are these obvious limitations to this system of classification.

Psychotic depression, on the other hand, is identical in every respect to a neurotic depression except that the patient's symptoms are more pronounced and his disease more incapacitating, for he has lost appreciable contact with reality. Again, psychiatry recognizes two main divisions of psychotic depression: manic-depressive and affective pyschosis. It is my personal conviction that most of these divisions of depression are of value primarily as a means of indicating the stage and severity of the disease rather than suggesting a different cause for each of these conditions. Psychotic depressions usually represent a continuum or linear progression of an unchecked or untreated neurotic depression. It would indicate that the destructive forces have become unbearable to the individual and his only escape is through fantasy and a dissociation of self from reality. In other words, a disease process which originally began as a minor or moderate illness has now progressed to a point of major threat to the individual's total personality and has rendered him, at least temporarily, unable to function in the human society. For our purpose, we will use the general term depression to connote all of its various forms and minifestations.

Signs and Symptoms of Depression

Depression can be defined as an emotional syndrome of varying degrees and causes in which the individual gradually loses his sense of self-worth and personal esteem. Psychiatry textbooks enumerate the signs and symptoms of depression in much greater detail. Dr. John J. Schwab lists at least thirty-six psychosomatic symptoms that are frequently found in patients suffering from depression. After reading this list, one is immediately impressed at how this emotional syndrome can effect nearly any facet of the patient's somatic, cognitive, or emotional system. It could be said that he who understands depression understands the major aspect of all emotional illness. The signs of depression are relatively few in comparison with its symptoms. They would include the mask of depression—the saddened countenance, sunken eyes, and vacant stare. Additional signs would include a shuffling gait, careless dress, halting speech, dry lips, and cold and expressionless hands. If, however, the patient were in a state of agitated depression, his observable signs would include angry eyes, rapid speech, tight lips, sweating palms, and constant or repetitive hand motions suggesting the uncontrollable urge to be on the move.

The symptoms of depression, according to Dr. Schwab, fall rather neatly into three general categories: affective, behavioral, and somatic manifestations. "The affective symptoms include: lowered mood, pessimism, dissatisfaction, helplessness, hopelessness; the somatic symptoms: insomnia, weight loss, palpitations, constipation and anorexia [appetite loss]; the behavioral symptoms: crying, retardation, and social withdrawal."[26] Add to this a long list of physical complaints, dryness of the skin and mouth, loss of hair, body pain, headache, and fatigue.

The Dynamics of Depression

The mechanism for these extremes in human moods and reactions can be found to reside mainly within the interplay of four sets of opposing forces: acceptance and rejection, gain and loss, comfort and discomfort, forgiveness and guilt. If these dynamic couplets are divided into their obvious polar groups and the vectors of acceptance, gain, comfort, and forgiveness are put in one cluster, with rejection, loss, discomfort, and guilt in another, we would find that those in the first group contain dynamic elements capable of exerting a positive or creative force upon the individual, and those in the second group would be recognized as having the potential for exerting a negative or destructive effect. From this we could conclude that if the preponderance of these several forces acting upon an individual were of a positive nature, it would evoke a feeling of happiness and fulfillment. And conversely, if the majority of these forces were negative, then the reaction would likely be one of sadness and dejection. Moreover, we could assume that if these negative forces were of sufficient intensity, number, and duration, they would give rise to depression.

Perhaps it is worthwhile to digress in order to clarify the terms rejection, loss, discomfort, and guilt, which are primarily responsible for producing both unhappiness and depression.

The dynamics of rejection have been discussed at some length in Chapter 2, but one fact seems worth repeating: *Rejection must be considered to be the greatest single force responsible for the production of human depression.* To be rejected is to be made to feel inferior, unaccepta-

ble, unloved, and unwanted. And all attitudes of superiority—
spoken or unspoken—of a racial, intellectual, physical, or social
nature invokes the same damaging force upon the demeaned individual. Indifference, too, is a common and often overlooked lethal
manifestation of human rejection.

The second significant element in the development of depression
is the effect of loss. Loss encompasses everything material, physical,
and emotional in the human environment: the loss of wealth in the
form of money or property; the loss of a job with its concomitant
threat to one's financial security; the loss of health with the inability
to work or to play; the loss of sight, hearing, or the ability to speak;
the loss of limb or any other important bodily appendage. Women
who have had one or both breasts removed for cancer almost uni-
formly experience profound postoperative depression, even though
they may have learned that their malignancy was completely eradicated. Add to this the many forms of emotional loss arising from
severed interpersonal relationships: the loss of significant love objects through death or separation, and the incalculable trauma of
divorce. It is indeed unfortunate that Hollywood has created the
illusion that because divorce is so commonplace, it must therefore
be a relatively easy experience. But only those who have gone
through the agonies of divorce can testify to its intrinsically painful
and destructive nature.

The third important force that frequently contributes to the in-
ducement of depression is discomfort. Immediately we think of pain
with its myriad manifestations. At least five considerations should
be employed in evaluating painful stimuli: the character or nature
of the stimulus, the intensity, the duration, the individual's pain
threshold or tolerance, and his reaction to pain. It is beyond the
scope of this book to discuss these parameters of pain and all of its
many neurophysiological and psychological aspects. Suffice it to say
that pain of sufficient intensity and duration is a significant factor in
the production of depression. Those who suffer from acute or
chronic disease and those lying wounded on battlefields will offer

convincing testimony to this fact. Yet human discomfort is not limited solely to the dynamics of physical pain. Pain has many emotional counterparts—anxiety, fear, frustration and fatigue—all of which add additional dimensions to man's *dis*–ease.

A fourth negative force is guilt. Guilt could easily have been included in the category of discomfort, but it plays a unique and important role in the creation of depression.

We have already discussed some of the salient features about the formation of guilt from both a theological and a psychological perspective. It was emphasized that a feeling of responsibility was an integral part of the guilt phenomenon as well as the Freudian concept of the superego chastening the ego in reprisal for unacceptable actions or thoughts. Noyes and Kolb in their text, *Modern Clinical Psychiatry*, place a great deal of emphasis upon the role of guilt in the production of depression. They say, "Depression has its roots in unconscious guilt arising from interpersonal issues, perhaps from unconscious ambivalence and hostility with resentful and aggressive impulses directed toward persons who are objects of their undesired obligation (a mother whose dependency prevents her daughter's marriage) or toward persons on whom one is dependent for security. The hostile impulses originally directed against other persons become directed against one's own self."[27] It is not necessary to accept all or any of these concepts for the mechanism of guilt formation, but it is most important to recognize that guilt is a frequent and significant participant in producing depression.

The Treatment of Depression

Recognition of the various causes of depression provides the basis for its treatment. We need only to look at the remaining half of our dynamic couplets and view the positive forces that remain: acceptance, gain, comfort, and forgiveness. Each of these elements can override the negative force and evoke a creative as well as a healing response within the individual. If this were not so, man's situation would indeed be hopeless. Each of these positive elements therefore becomes a specific antidote for its destructive or negative counterpart.

It is precisely at this point that telotherapy offers its unique and therapeutic power. It has the ability to provide acceptance, not only on a human level, but on a human-divine level as well. Telotherapy can help the patient to find a new love object called God, who can sustain him during and after his quest for new existential love objects. Telotherapy can offer the direction toward an inner comfort called peace, which the world cannot give. And telotherapy can offer the direction and the guideposts by which the suffering individual can find forgiveness from the actions or nonactions that have created his guilt. I do not mean to infer that the treatment of depression should therefore become the exclusive responsibility of the telotherapist, or that telotherapy alone provides the only effective means for its amelioration. Overcoming depression requires the cooperative efforts of all therapeutic disciplines, both present and future. I only hope that many people will learn and adopt this effective method of treating this human malady.

Any discussion of depression should include a few remarks about suicide, which is frequently the end-product of depression. Any successful or unsuccessful attempt at suicide should tell us several things. It represents not only an expression of ultimate hostility toward one's self or toward society, as psychiatrists suggest, but it also says that the individual has reached his point of maximum endurance and can see no solution for his despair—except death. Suicide is not, as many fundamental religionists would want us to believe, a heinous and an unforgivable sin. Self-destruction is always a sad occasion and represents, as far as this life is concerned, a tragic and unfulfilling human act. But this does not render it an action unworthy of God's forgiveness. Suicide is not the negation of total life; it must be viewed as merely representing the termination of the existential phase of total life. Suicide must also be seen as the result of society's failure to fulfill the needs of the individual as much as the individual's inability to cope with his despair. We have only to recall the dynamics of depression to see society's role in this exterminating act. While the individual is indeed responsible for much of his emotional and spiritual health, for too long society has merely pointed a wagging finger of condemnation toward the suicide victim with the idea that it is in no way implicated in his demise. Yet society must recognize and admit its complicity, and must change its role from one of destruction to one of healing.

I hope that this discussion of depression will help you to see more clearly the special role that telotherapy has to offer in treating emotional illness. Moreover, I hope that those who would apply this concept would be able to realize some of the following conclusions. First, spiritual and mental illness are so closely allied and interrelated that separation on the basis of signs and symptoms is not only unnecessary but impossible. Both conditions often present in a similar manner, and frequently as depression. So the possibility for differentiation between these two conditions lies solely in the patient's account of his illness and the therapist's ability to perceive the origins of his suffering. And only those therapists who recognize a spiritual dimension in man will be able to make this essential distinction. Second, although telotherapy directs its major therapeutic thrust toward the nuclear portion of the atom (in our abstract illustration) and attempts to heal the rift in the God-man relationship, it cannot escape getting involved in the peripheral dynamics of the human personality as well. Just as the environmental factors exert an effect upon the nucleus, so the nuclear components affect the elements of the environment. Third, a mature God-man relationship not only acts as a therapeutic force in mental illness, it can also provide significant protection for the individual, in a preventive sense, against the ravages of mental illness. Fourth, the telotherapist enters into the therapeutic arena in a manner similar, though not identical, to the therapist who applies psychological techniques —through the door of patient acceptance. Fifth, telotherapy offers the patient a healing force that applied psychology, in and of itself, cannot offer. And sixth, telotherapy has the potential to heal not only spiritual illness, but many forms of mental illness as well.

Another means of projecting the close proximity and interrelatedness of spiritual and mental illness is to view the etiologic dynamics of non-organic mental illness primarily from the perspective of human love deprivation rather than from the traditional vantage of Freudian or neo-Freudian psychology. This approach will undoubtedly appear to the more sophisticated minds as a simplistic and naïve explanation for an enormously complex human syndrome. Nevertheless, I believe it provides a practical method for understanding some of the major contributing factors in many cases of mental illness. Mental illness can frequently be traced to a significant interference with the *normal human love cycle*. This love cycle is of measurable duration and has a readily discernible pattern of growth and development. It extends from birth to death and encompasses all of existential life. Its development begins at the time of birth with love being bestowed upon the individual as a newborn infant by both of his parents. This experience is subsequently followed by the individual's response of reciprocating love toward his parents. From infancy on this cycle of human love continuously expands to include being loved and loving all other members of the greater family circle—such as siblings, grandparents, aunts, uncles, and so forth. Later, the love cycle extends beyond the immediate family constellation to include all significant persons within the individual's total existential environment. As this individual approaches adulthood, his love usually focuses prodominantly upon a particular member of the opposite sex which eventually, through the process of dating and engagement, results in marriage. With marriage comes children, and once again the cycle of human love begins for another new life. But it does not end for the parents, it merely continues in an ever-increasingly complex form until the moment of death is reached. There are, however, many modifying factors, both intrinsic and extrinsic, which tend to interfere with the development of this normal human love cycle. Many of these factors can be identified and measured in a quantitative and qualitative manner. Others cannot. Some of these modifying influences will serve to accelerate and support the normal development of this human love cycle, but most act as deterrents. Some of these forces which would inhibit the growth of human love would include such things as a deficiency in both the amount and kind of love which is bestowed upon the infant by his parents and how the individual chooses to respond to the love he receives from his family and the many other persons he encounters within his human environment. One frequent human impediment in this love cycle is the individual's selfishness which is expressed in his refusal to love others while demanding to be loved by others. And there is also the devastating effect of the individual who is constantly rejected by others —who never has his love recognized nor accepted in a reciprocal fashion. Or, the individual who is simply loved by no one in his environment. All of these factors impair the development of the human love cycle and prevent the formation of good mental health.

Even upon quick examination, it can be seen that every individual is therefore dependent on the people within his family constellation and many significant persons in his environment for the development of his love cycle. Without this vital human support, his chances for developing a normal love cycle and avoiding the agonies of mental illness would be extremely slim and the likelihood for happiness remote. So once again we can see the juxtaposition of spiritual and mental illness—with spiritual illness stemming from the individual's failure to respond to God's love and mental illness coming as the result of an interruption in the development of the normal human love cycle. And when we ponder the belief expressed by David Roberts, ". . . that divine and human love cannot be fulfilled apart from each other," these two human maladies become even more closely intertwined. If his statement is true, it poses the very basic question of whether mature mental health can ever by achieved without an appropriate response to God's love.

Until now, nothing has been said about the contagious nature of spiritual illness—only its frequency. There is a direct correlation between these two factors, for it is the highly transmissible character of spiritual illness that makes its overall incidence so prodigious. Two clinical illustrations will substantiate this point.

Mrs. W. was a forty-seven-year-old white female who was as charming as she was attractive. She was petite and poised. She came to my office upon referral from a dermatologist to have a complete physical examination. She related her problem in the following manner. She had, over the past twelve to eighteen months, been losing large quantities of her hair. She had seen several physicians, but all treatment seemed to be of no avail. The first dermatologist had thought her condition was the result of a local infection of the hair follicles and had prescribed several lotions and creams containing various combinations of antibiotics and corticosteroids. She had applied them conscientiously to her scalp two and three times a day for several months, but with little visible benefit. So she had gone to see another dermatologist, who told her that he felt her condition was not due to a localized infection of her scalp or hair follicles, but was most probably a manifestation of a systemic illness, perhaps a thyroid deficiency. For that reason, he sent her on to me for a complete medical evaluation. It was not until she removed her wig that I became acutely aware of the extent of her problem. Her hair was indeed thin, cut very short and there were two large circular areas of almost total baldness; one in the front and another in the back of her head. Both of these areas measured four to five inches in diameter. What a traumatic experience, I thought, for such an otherwise extremely attractive woman! Certainly her wig was her social salvation.

I examined her literally from the top of her head to the soles of her feet, inside and out. I could find no evidence of organic disease that would account for her hair loss. There were no discernible endocrine deficiencies, no obvious electrolyte imbalance, no anemia, and no suggestion of any metabolic disease. I then shifted my investigation into the psychological and spiritual aspects of her life.

Mrs. W. was the wife of a very successful corporation attorney, a well-known civic leader who was active in the higher echelon of city politics. They had been married twenty-six years and had two children both of whom were now married and living in neighboring states. She described her marriage as being "just one big party after another." As far back as she could recall, her role was to be a charming hostess and to support her husband's business and social aspirations. The children were more or less kept in the background until they were older and had developed a sufficient degree of social poise so as not to detract from the image of their father. Mrs. W. admitted that she had enjoyed participating in these charades for the first few years of their marriage, because she had come from a modest environment and all this seemed to be like "one huge Hollywood dream." But somewhere along the line, the dream began to wear thin. It began when her husband insisted upon getting the children out of sight or sent them off to the movies whenever important guests were due. And she could not attend her children's school programs because of "more important social engagements." And when it became apparent that the frequency with which just the two of them would be alone, to make love and to enjoy one another's company, were getting less and less frequent, even after the children were away, she became dismayed. She now felt that she and her children had been used and exploited in order to promote her husband's advancements and to perpetuate his image of being a "Mr. Everything." All of these thought had been piling up in her mind to the point where she could no longer sleep without medication, go out in public without taking a tranquilizer, and no longer converse with her husband without getting either angry or crying. She said their meals were spent sitting at opposite ends of a long table: he watching television, she not saying a word. At night, they slept in different rooms. At parties, they would say a few words to each other beforehand, nothing throughout the evening, and then argue on the way home over who had the most to drink. All this, and much more, had left her with a terrible emptiness. She felt hurt, angry, and as though life had no meaning.

Fortunately, I had one session with her husband. (Usually the male partner of the marriage team fails to show and most often refuses to think of himself as being a part of either the problem or the solution.) Mr. W. was everything his wife had said. He was impeccably dressed, articulate, and had the bearing of a "Philadelphia lawyer." He lacked only the spats, the cane, and the gold cigarette holder. He was obviously well educated, and informed me within the first few minutes of our meeting that he had graduated from Harvard Law School. In fact, he was so suave that I immediately began to feel quite inferior. I momentarily succumbed to the temptation to play his game of wit, but it soon became obvious to both of us that I was losing. I was no match for him. I thought it really should be he who was interviewing me rather than the reverse, and I feel sure that he felt the same way. Needless to say, the entire hour was spent on a very superficial plane as he adroitly manipulated most of the conversation. But I was still able to get a fairly good overview of what it was about him that was bothering his wife. Everytime I interjected anything about his wife's condition, he would merely brush it off with some trite comment such as "the little woman has always been prone to these nervous spells. Just like her mother, you know." Or, "if she'd just quit pulling at her hair, she would be all right." And so it went, pretty much like that Hollywood dream the patient had described. So predictable were his answers that I almost had to pinch myself to make sure that I was not viewing a late show on television. His concluding remarks were succinct, "Well, if you can't fix her up, doctor, I'm sure we can find someone else who can."

Mrs. B. was a sixty-three-year-old white female who came to my office once a month in a wheelchair. She was badly crippled with arthritis and relied almost entirely upon her husband for her mobility. Two years ago, I assisted with her gastrectomy for a bleeding ulcer. On the surface, Mrs. B. appeared to be calm and serene, looking for all the world like she had accepted her infirmity with "good Christian courage." But beneath this facade was a seething and angry woman who couldn't find a good thing to say about anybody and who complained about everything. In her defense, it would only be fair to say that Mrs. B. had been unlucky. Her initial attack of arthritis began at age twenty-two following the birth of her first child. The second attack came after the stillbirth of her second child. And her third episode was coincidental with the death of her father. From that time on, her arthritis had never left her and now involved almost every weight-bearing joint of her body, as well as her hands. Until a year ago, she had been able to crochet despite her misshapen and painful joints. But now, although much of her pain had subsided, she was unable to hold her crochet needles firmly enough to allow her to do any work.

One could scarcely blame Mrs. B. for her despair and her anger. Life certainly seemed to have inflicted upon her a disproportionate amount of suffering. But her physical disability was a red herring. Neither the ulcer nor the arthritis was the real cause. Mrs. B. had an unhappy marriage. Her husband, a branch manager of a community bank, was difficult to live with. Outwardly he was a bright and charming individual who slapped people on the back and called everyone by his first name. He ran a good bank. He was a trustee in his church and he sang in the sanctuary choir. Yet inwardly he was a very self-centered and uncharitable man. He detested his wife's infirmity and let her know "often and in no uncertain terms" how she was an impediment to his progress and how fortunate she was to have someone who would wait on her hand and foot. He constantly inferred that much of her real problem was in her mind and that she wasn't as disabled as she let on. The constant jibes and stinging sarcasm had, according to Mrs. B., "burned a hole right through her heart." When she first began her therapy, she had been relying on alcohol and barbiturates to reduce her inner tensions. For this, her husband called her a "spineless lush."

In addition to demonstrating the contagious nature of spiritual illness, these two cases reveal some of its potentially destructive characteristics as well. Fortunately, neither Mrs. W. nor Mrs. B. ever became psychotic, but both did contract, in addition to their husband's spiritual illness, significant manifestations of mental and organic disease.

The last case shows telotherapy in operation and demonstrates a totally unstructured application of its healing power. It was a situation in which neither the therapists nor the patients were consciously aware of the healing dynamics that were being administered. This case was told to me by a physician who was at that time the chief of psychiatry at one of the state mental hospitals.

One day the psychiatrist received a phone call at his office from a woman who said she was the president of the Women's Guild at one of the local Lutheran churches. Her group was looking for an opportunity to serve the community and wondered if he had any patients in the mental institution who would appreciate regular visits from the women. He replied that there were many such patients, and if the women would come to the hospital, he would allow them to work with an entire ward of disturbed but noncombative female patients.

The ward to which he assigned these women contained twenty-two patients. Most of them had been hospitalized there for periods of two to five years, and some for as long as seven years. Their illnesses varied, but all were suffering from a form of major mental illness. All were, or had been, grossly psychotic. Many were diagnosed as schizophrenics of paranoid, catatonic, and hebephrenic varieties. Some were manic-depressives. Others were thought to be suffering from advanced forms of senile dementia due to organic brain disease. In nearly every case, they were predominantly out of contact with reality and had little or no concept of time and place. The degree of personality and behavioral decomposition also varied. Fifteen of these patients were so removed from reality that they would defecate or urinate on the floor or upon themselves. Many would remove all of their clothes if "the room got too hot," or for no reason at all. They had lost nearly all sense of appropriateness. Few of these fifteen patients would bathe or even troubled to wash their hands or face. Meals were often consumed in a manner that would be an embarrassment to any domesticated animal. Dirty hands, rather than utensils, were used to convey the food from the plate to their mouths, and much was lost in transit. The other seven patients still retained some semblance of humanity and maintained a fair degree of personal hygiene and dress.

However, the overall condition of these patients was pretty miserable. It reminded one of some of the classical descriptions of the "snake pits" at or near the turn of the century, with a few modern innovations. Moreover, these patients would present a formidable challenge to any group of medically or psychologically trained individuals, but an even greater challenge to untrained do-gooders from the local church. The psychiatrist admitted that he had purposely given these women this particular ward because of the seeming hopelessness of the patients' conditions and because he knew that they got very little attention from the hospital personnel. Most of the professional staff members, including himself, could scarcely tolerate the odor within the ward. Electroshock, medication, and limited psychotherapy had already been administered, with very little discernible improvement.

After meeting with the women, the psychiatrist decided that a team of four to six women could come twice weekly for a period of four hours—from 2 to 6 P.M.—and again for two hours every Sunday afternoon, During this period of time, the women would help the patients bathe, groom their hair and fingernails, and then apply as much facial cosmetics as each patient desired. They would also dress them properly and help them repair any of their torn or worn-out clothing. The women would frequently play records of both popular and classical music on a little portable phonograph or merely sit and hold the patient's hand while watching a television program. Sometimes they would encourage the patients to make things with their hands, like a simple potholder or handkerchief. But most often the patients preferred to just sit and string beads. Some patients would be encourged to draw or paint. And sometimes the women from the church would read passages from the Bible, especially from the Psalms or from the Sermon on the Mount, though no attempt was made to "convert" or "Christianize" them.

The members of this women's guild persisted in their visiting, loving, and reconstructive efforts for five consecutive months. At the conclusion of this time six patients were deemed well enough to be discharged to their homes and families. Eight patients were considered adequately improved to be transferred from the closed to the open ward. And of the remaining eight only two seemed virtually unchanged.

No one was more surprised than the psychiatrist. He found the results almost unbelievable. The thing that provided an additional interest was the fact that this psychiatrist, like so many of his colleagues, is a self-acknowledged agnostic and a rather inflexible Freudian.

It would be wrong to assume from this therapeutic experiment that these patients had been incorrectly diagnosed. But the results of these women's efforts force us to speculate on several possibilities. First, the favorable response upon the part of many of these patients provides significant evidence that nonorganic mental and spiritual illness often coexist and the human and *agape* love that these women transmitted to these patients had an undeniably beneficial therapeutic effect. Secondly, many varieties of organic as well as nonorganic mental illness seem to respond to this combination of human and *agape* love, and so application of these forms of love should always be an integral part of their treatment. A third possibility may be due to the fact that the women had broken these patients' virtual isolation from the outside world. By their mere presence, they had brought a new hope and a new will to live.

5

A Christian View of Man

As we have discussed, telotherapy is a method of diagnosing and treating spiritual illness. We have defined what is meant by spiritual illness and how telotherapy is applied. It is now appropriate to get a firm grasp of a Christian view of man. Without this theological perspective the dynamics of telotherapy will remain obscure and never come into sharp focus.

Theology deals with a special realm of faith and knowledge. It is a systematic attempt to explain the human experience of God. Tillich says, "A theological system is supposed to satisfy two basic needs: the statement of truth of the Christian message and the interpretation of this truth for every new generation."[28] Theology also emphasizes the dynamic features of this God-man relationship in order to convey the constant movement that underlies this interaction. Serious errors are made in creating a static concept of this relationship. Theology must always be moving and expanding in order to keep pace with the tempo and needs of existential life. To paraphrase a statement by Jesus, theology was made for man and not man for theology. Yet all adequate theologies must convey the central truth that all of life is lived in realtionship to God, and only in proportion to our ability to apprehend this truth is our degree of contact with reality determined. But the preciseness of this relationship always eludes man's capture, thereby making any and all theologies incomplete. The uniqueness of Christian theology, however, which places it above other theologies, lies in the fact that it centers all of its doctrines upon the belief that Jesus of Nazareth was indeed the Christ and the human expression of God.

But it must be recognized at the onset that there is no one theology, even within the Christian faith, that satisfies all believers. The dichotomy between the Catholic and Protestant divisions of Christianity is perpetuated because of many differences in doctrinal interpretations. However, in many cases, these differences are no greater than some of those that exist between many of the denominations within the Protestant church itself or among the Roman Catholic orders. Fortunately, many of these differences and those of an interdenominational nature seem to have been disappearing over the years and the chance for greater unity within all facets of Christianity seems more hopeful. But there is no need to resolve all of these intrafaith or even interfaith differences before accepting the therapeutic principles of telotherapy. Telotherapy does not require, either on the part of the therapist or the patient, a specific belief in a particular form of theology or even in a Christian theology in order to effectively administer or receive its therapeutic benefits. If this were not true, the prognosis for those suffering from spiritual illness would be extremely poor.

The application of telotherapy is universal. It is predicated upon the healing love of God that transcends all religions and all faiths. Admittedly, the dynamics of telotherapy in this book are expressed within the framework of Christian theology, which I believe fulfills all the criteria of a meaningful and valid theology. But this does not exclude those outside of the Christian faith. Jesus did not refuse to heal the centurian's boy because his father was a Roman soldier. Jesus could only marvel at the man's "faith" and immediately healed his child. Furthermore, it must be recognized that spiritual illness can strike anyone. No one—Christian or non-Christian—is exempt from its contagious and potentially destructive qualities.

Here I only want to provide a brief outline of the nature of man as viewed from a Christian perspective. As this concept is developed our attention will be focused most specifically upon those dynamic features of Christian theology that pertain to the diagnosis and treatment of spiritual illness. Moreover, our study of telotherapy will show how spiritual illness can be prevented as well as cured.

From a theological perspective of faith, the cycle of total life has three distinct phases. It begins with the eternal, proceeds to the temporal, and returns to the eternal. Total life begins with the process of creation by God, which precedes and supersedes the advent of bisexual conception and human reproduction. Creation takes place in the realm of the eternal, or in heaven, if you will. The second phase is the earthly, temporal, or existential phase. This segment begins with human conception, with the uniting of the sperm with the ovum, developing on through birth and ending at the moment of physical death. This temporal span is the one with which we are best acquainted and most concerned, and appears to be the *only* part of life to those who lack this theological concept of total life. The third and final phase of total life is the return to the eternal. This transition from the temporal to the eternal occurs at the moment of physical death and implies our reunion with our Creator. Each of these three phases of total life is important and applies to us who reside in the temporal phase of the cycle.

In the creation segment of total life we are given our essence or all of our potential to become mature creatures of God. This portion of our creation has nothing whatsoever to do with our potential for becoming musicians, architects, writers, scientists, or athletes. That potential is derived from our genetic storehouse, which does not make its contribution to our uniqueness until the beginning of the second phase. This theological concept of creation has several basic elements that provide much of the foundation for understanding the dynamics of spiritual growth and development. It also serves as an integral part in the process of telotherapy.

There are some of the more salient features believed to be intrinsic and unique to the essential nature of man. These elements within our divine or essential nature are manifested both in terms of faith or "felt awareness" as well as fulfilling all the cognitive criteria, a priori, for any proposition of theological truth. First, there is a faith, and then a knowledge, of our constant and nondepreciating individual worth in the sight of God. Second, a faith and knowledge of our equalness to all other human creatures in the judgment of God. Third, the faith and knowledge that total life is a gift from God.

Fourth, the faith and knowledge that each of us has the potential for becoming Christlike individuals, the intrinsic capacity to approach Christ's exemplary degree of human and spiritual maturation. Fifth, the faith and knowledge that each of us bears the irrevocable image of God's creation and nothing whatsoever can erase its indelible nature. Sixth, a faith and knowledge that our creation is intrinsically good, and therefore as humans we always contain the potential for being good. Seventh, the faith and knowledge that there is a constant flow of divine love (*agape*) and reason (*logos*) from God to man that begins at the moment of our creation and extends throughout Eternal Life. Eighth, the faith and knowledge that our ultimate destiny is predetermined within the process of our creation and that each of us will participate in the third and final phase of total life.

Because of differing interpretations of the Scriptures and varying degrees of theological enlightenment, not all of these propositions will be found acceptable to all Christian scholars or clergy. However, I think that most of these propositions are implied if not explicit within the Christian doctrine of creation and are generally accepted in most contemporary theological circles. These eight propositions will provide the foundation for understanding the significance of the essential nature of man and be used as a solid basis for comprehending some of the dynamic interrelationships that confront man during his period of existential experience.

The second or existential phase of total life is both a continuum of the first phase and a prelude to the final phase of total life. This fact cannot be overemphasized nor should it ever be dismissed from the conceptual image of the Christian view of man. It is in man's beginning and in his ultimate destiny that meaning, direction, and purpose to existential life is to be found. Unfortunately, many nineteenth- and early twentieth-century theologians and clergymen interpreted this to mean that existential life was therefore relatively unimportant in the full spectrum of life. They viewed existential life in rather passive terms and implied that it was merely an interim phase that man had to endure before he gained his ultimate reward of entering into the Kingdom of Heaven. But upon a new and closer look by contemporary theologians, such as Tillich and Niebuhr, existential life is seen as man's greatest and most formidable challenge. It was, they said, never meant to be a passive experience but one that requires man's total and unrelenting participation. With this newer perspective, the primary emphasis of the Christian life which had seemingly been centered chiefly in escaping life and seeking personal salvation has now shifted into a broader and more ecumenical manner of thinking. Christianity can now be expressed in terms of recognizing, accepting, and transmitting the love of God in such a manner as to give all men the opportunity to experience the abundance of the unified life.

Classical orthodox theology explains man's initial encounter with life through the story of the Garden of Eden and introduces some of the material upon which the Christian doctrines of creation, fall, and original sin have been structured. Actually, this mythical story does an excellent job with symbols and metaphors in giving a primitive and beautiful explanation of man's entrance into the world and his defiance of God. However, it must not be taken literally or it will create more enigmas than it seeks to clarify. But it remains that this story poignantly points out that God did indeed create man and woman. And God did provide man with a beautiful garden (or planet) upon which to live, a faith stance of singular importance. Furthermore, it is apparent from history that man has always sought to defy God and deny that he (God) had any claim upon his life. So the central truths in the Eden myth are valid from the standpoint of faith and only the knowledge of how man and nature were formed remain in question.

It seems reasonable to assume that in the Garden of Eden man symbolically experienced a combination of first and early second phases of total life. He was still intimately associated with God, a characteristic of the creation phase, but was at the same time beginning to express some of his relative freedom by resisting God's commandments, a characteristic of existential life. Yet in the Garden, man was still more essential than existential being. It was only after his forced exit that he became predominately existential.

Next to the metaphorical description of the creation of Adam and Eve lies the story of man's "fall" or separation from God, presumably arising from man's disobedience—his eating the fruit of the tree of knowledge. Closer scrutiny of this entire interaction however, allows us to divide man's fall into two distinct segments. The first segment could be designated as God's intentional will, the second as God's permissive will. The first phase had nothing whatsoever to do with man's disobedience. It symbolizes the change from being a totally essential creature in the realm of the eternal to becoming a composite essential-existential creature in the realm of the temporal. This first segment of man's "fall" signals the advent of man's "becoming" and stepping out into existence, which is necessary if he is to become a real person. This does not represent, as many have supposed, the thrusting of man out of heaven or the Garden by an angry God.

The second segment of man's fall is of quite another nature. It occurred somewhat later in the existential stage of total life and is the direct result of man's willful disobedience of God's command. It symbolizes man's inappropriate response to God's love and a distortion of God's purpose for human life. This second segment closely adheres to the usual concept of man's "original sin" and the action that provided his expulsion from the Garden of Eden. It represent man's volitional separation from his Creator and is the result of promoting self-will ahead of God's will.

Within these two conceptual components resides the doctrine of man's fall and the origin of human sin. But Tillich qualifies the issue of sin by making it synonomous with man's separation from God, which includes both segments of man's fall. Man's sin, therefore, is the fact of his separation, and the challenge of existential life is to overcome this separation. It means that in order for man to approach his maximal capability as a creature of God upon earth, he must overcome his sin of separation and unify his existential being with his essential nature. This unity destroys the human-divine schizophrenia that inhibits man's existential life, rendering him free and fulfilled. This is what is implied by the doctrine of salvation. To be saved is to have overcome our basic separation from God. Salvation means to be made whole, to be made healthy and to be right with God. Salvation also means to be set free. These are but a few of the unique manifestations of the unified and unambiguous life.

Although the fundamental challenge of existential life and the desired goal of achieving the unified life has been mentioned, nothing has been said about how this might be accomplished. To approach an answer to this question, we must introduce an additional Christian doctrine intrinsic to the faith: grace. Grace is the means by which man receives both God's acceptance and forgiveness. Grace is the undeserved love of God. Grace makes the phenomenon of healing possible by providing the means whereby man can overcome his separation from God.

Christian theology also accepts the fact of man's dependent and finite nature. "Man," says Outler, "is finite and is, therefore, not *self*-sufficient or *self*-explanatory or *self*-fulfilled! No finite creature can be. But it is God's design for him—and, therefore, the human possibility—that he should grow up into sufficiency and fulfillment in God's providence and through his own trustful responding to God's grace."[29] This human finiteness and our dependency upon God becomes most apparent in our struggle to resolve the estrangement that exists between our human and divine self. Christian theology adamantly avers that man cannot overcome this alienation without God's help. And it is precisely at this point that the dual redeeming forces of God's grace, acceptance and forgiveness, enter into the picture of man's fulfillment. The miracle of acceptance and forgiveness paves the way to the unambiguous life and permits man to be healed of his spiritual illness.

The potential for this healing phenomenon has always been available to mankind. But its availability was never made more patently clear until the coming of Jesus. He clarified the dynamics of spiritual health and healing that are accessible to every human creature. This faith became the Christian gospel or the "good news" and the answer to the dilemma of human existence.

The third and final stage of total life is man's return to the realm of the eternal. Mystery shrouds both the exact mode and means of this return, but Christian theology adamantly affirms this terminal event and unhesitatingly attempts to disclose a portion of its nature and significance. And at the same time, contemporary theology heeds the warning offered by Niebuhr when he says, "It is unwise for Christians to claim any knowledge of either the furniture of heaven or the temperature of hell; or to be too certain about any details of the Kingdom of God in which history is consummated."[30] The specific details of this event are certainly lacking and probably, in the purpose of God, will always remain so. But it is necessary to know that Eternal Life is a part of reality and that God is the sovereign ruler of that realm. Outler expresses his views about this last phase of life when he says, "The Christian hope of immortality includes a very realistic idea of death—of real extinction—but matches it with the strong affirmation that God who gave us life wills to renew it, in ways quite past finding out, but with the same consummatory love and power which we know and have shared in creation and redemption."[31]

Any discussion of Eternal Life immediately poses many questions. Does everyone, good and bad, participate in Eternal Life? If so, how are the righteous rewarded any more than the unrighteous? If not, who is to be accepted and who rejected? And what happens to those who might be rejected? What is the role of God's judgment and man's existential behavior in determining the opportunity to participate in this final dimension of life? What is meant by the term "Kingdom of God" and how does it differ from Eternal Life?

Neither Jesus, nor his apostles, nor the prophets before them ever provided clear and unequivocal answers to all of these questions. Honest and searching theologians have attempted to synthesize from all of the fragmentary knowledge available to them the most rational or suprarational conclusions about the nature of life after death. They have also projected an idea of "majestic reasonableness," which would be in keeping with the total concept of a loving God. Again, what is to follow is not accepted by all Christians; yet this understanding represents a composite of the thoughts expressed by Tillich, Niebuhr, Bonhoeffer, Ferré, and others who seem to reflect this high degree of majestic reasonableness in their interpretations of eternal life. Furthermore, I believe that their thoughts are very much in keeping with our ever-broadening concept of the limitless love of God.

Tillich's concept of "essentialization" and universal participation of all men in Eternal Life seems extremely plausible and seems to meet most of the criteria of theological credibility. Universal essentialization is the process of God's ultimate judgment in which he strips away from each individual that which is negative or evil and retains only that which is positive or good. Only the positive elements accompany the individual into Eternal Life. Yet the experience of essentialization neither removes the sting of God's condemnation of our sin nor deprives us of our rewards for our more noble earthly efforts. Both remain untouched and undiminished within the process of transcendent essentialization. The shame and despair arising at the moment of our confrontation with the evil within us is still an integral and painful part of God's judgment of our existential behavior. But it is because of God's mercy and forgiving grace that man survives this judgment and sustains his unity with God. It is always God's forgiveness rather than man's virtue that forms the basis for his participation in eternal life. Nor does God fail to reward those for a job well done. The reward is manifested in the abundance of positive elements that one will be allowed to bring with him into the third dimension of total life.

This concept of universal essentialization does away with the idea of the absolute dualistic destiny of "heaven or hell," "saved or lost," "eternal blessedness or eternal damnation." It further precludes the need for such concepts as "reincarnation," "purgatory," or "intermediary states."

Little of a definite nature can be said about the form of each individual who participates in Eternal Life other than that he undoubtedly assumes a spiritual and nonfinite quality. What this means is purely speculative. Whether or not we retain any of our unique earthly characteristics is also unknown. But we can be cer-

tain that whatever this new form takes, it will be superior to anything
we have ever known or conceived.

Any discussion of Eternal Life that deletes the associated eschato-
logical symbol of the coming of the Kingdom of God is incomplete
and subtracts from the total spectrum of Christian theology. Most
serious theologians seem to feel that the symbol of the coming of
the Kingdom of God represents the ushering in of the end of history
and the fulfillment of God's creation. It becomes both the *finis* and
the *telos*. Furthermore, its coming has political, social, individual,
and universal implications that will affect all of God's creatures. The
arrival of the Kingdom of God will represent an immediate and
indivisible unity between the consummation of human history and
Eternal Life.

Hence this deeper level of Christian theology upon which much
of telotherapy is predicated views life as having three distinct but
interrelated phases: creation, existential life, and eternal life.

Between the questions "where from" and "where to" lies the whole system
of theological questions and answers. But it is not simply a straight line
from the one to the other. The relation is more intrinsic; "where to" is
inseparably implied in the "where from"; the meaning of creation is revealed in its end. And conversely, the nature of the "where to" is determined by the nature of the "where from"; that is, only the valuation of the
creation as good makes an eschatology of fulfillment possible; and only the
idea of fulfillment makes the creation meaningful.[32]

6

A Theology of Acceptance and Fulfillment

Things would indeed be more simple if all people would agree to accept the Christian theology we have just put forth as a foundation for understanding our man-God relationship. But not all people are in accord with this or with any other explicit concept that deals with a description of man's interaction with God. Preeminent among the many reasons for this is the abstract nature of theology, which makes proof of any of its concepts virtually impossible, including the very existence of God. Another is the fact that man's understanding of existential life and God are constantly changing. These two reasons alone make it easy to see why there is so little unanimity of agreement even in the most basic doctrines of the Christian faith.

It appears that nearly each person in every generation seems to feel the need to delete, modify, or somehow reconstruct the traditional theology of the previous generation into one that more adequately coincides with his understanding of the Creator and the meaning of life. Therefore, any theology—fundamental, orthodox, neoorthodox, Christian or non-Christian—that fails to allow for these adjustments will end up being an anachronism in any rapidly changing society and will cease to speak to the members of the "now generation." Men like Martin Luther King, Jr., Harvey Cox, and William Stringfellow are, or have been, acutely aware of this need to keep Christian theology relevant and practical. They have, each in their own way, been involved in developing a contemporary social theology, one that underscores the need for total Christian commitment as a requirement for resolving some of the pressing social problems that may destroy our human society.

Theologian Sam Keen and clergyman Malcolm Boyd have independently structured and promoted a visceral theology that they
feel speaks to people on a "gut level." In *To a Dancing God*, Keen
seems to be reacting rather vociferously over the stance taken by
traditional theology on the corrupt nature of man. For him, this
attitude about the inherent depravity of man is repugnant and un-
tenable. Moreover, he seems to find that this term draws the line
between traditional theism and contemporary humanism. (For me,
it clearly delineates one of the basic differences between telotherapy
and psychotherapy.) Keen poses the critical question: Is man corrupt or merely immature? He says,

> There is an immense theoretical as well as functional difference between
> the view that man is corrupt and therefore in need of salvation and the view
> that he is immature or weak and needs to grow up. If the human predica-
> ment is seen as serious, critical, a matter of life and death, then radical
> therapy is not only appropriate but morally necessary. If on the other hand,
> the difference between the best and the worst of men is a matter of degrees
> rather than of kind, the therapy prescribed for the ailing will be less severe.
> Traditional Christianity, romanticism, Marxism, and the hippies see a radi-
> cal discontinuity between sinner and saved, corrupt and innocent, exploiter
> and exploited, the square and the hip. Each calls for some form of radical
> therapy: conversion, new birth, ideological revolution, turning on, becom-
> ing enlightened, passing from darkness into light. Depth psychology, hu-
> manistic wisdom and common sense see the indefinite shades of gray that
> distinguish the wise and the foolish, the mature and the immature. They
> know the darkness that remains in the hearts of the enlightened as well as
> the moments of lucidity and kindness that surprise the dullest of human
> beings. Growth rather than conversion is therefore the remedy they pre-
> scribe for all men.[33]

Keen carefully, and I think purposely, avoids offering a solution
to this succinct polemic, for reasons that are not entirely clear.
Nevertheless, it seems imperative to attempt to answer this crucial
question, which is fundamental to a grasp of telotherapy. This
proposition delineates the differences between telotherapy, which
is theistic in its orientation, from the many forms of psychotherapy,
which are humanistic in their orientations. My answer is that man

does indeed stand in need of salvation not because he is corrupt, but because he is unfulfilled as a result of his separation from God, "the ground of all being" (Tillich). Furthermore, man is also immature. He is emotionally, intellectually, and spiritually immature. So to answer Dr. Keen more concisely: it isn't a matter of either-or; it is a matter of both. Man is both unfulfilled and immature and it will require the combined efforts of telotherapy and psychology to assist him as he moves toward fulfillment and maturation.

During my struggle in the formulation and synthesis of this therapeutic approach to spiritual illness, I found it necessary to develop yet another theology, one that is simple to enunciate yet profound enough to lead patients toward the depth of theological understanding that Tillich and others provide. I have called this modification a theology of acceptance and fulfillment. It is a theology that expresses a positive evaluation of man rather than a negative one. It views man as being basically acceptable rather than corrupt and condemned. Norman Vincent Peale may have taken undue liberties with Christian theology when he developed his theology of success, but at least he noticed one important trait in the human organism: man responds more readily and more favorably in many situations when he adopts a positive rather than a negative outlook on life. Likewise, people will respond more readily to a theology that finds them acceptable rather than one that condemns them.

It must be clearly understood that what is to follow is neither an original nor a complete theology. It is merely a theology that places a fresh emphasis upon two of the most salient features found in the Christian gospel. But I hope that this adaptation will find a new relevance in our contemporary society that much traditional orthodox theology seems to lack. This theology is not meant to replace any of the more complete or mature systematic theologies of Tillich, Barth, Niebuhr, and others; it is merely constructed to woo the reader beyond this superficial presentation and to dig more deeply into the works of these theologians. This theology of acceptance and fulfillment was synthesized chiefly for telotherapy and is designed to assist those who suffer from spiritual illness.

The dynamics of the two central ingredients of this theology, acceptance and fulfillment, can be rather briefly stated; yet it is essential that one recognize the sequential development within and between these two vital components. Acceptance usually precedes participation in the abundant life that prepares man for the ultimate gift of fulfillment.

Acceptance has its own orderly scheme of development, which includes: the acceptance by God, the acceptance of God, the acceptance of self, and the acceptance of others. Hopefully, we will be able to show that both self-acceptance and the ability to accept others is predicated mainly, though not exclusively, upon the individual's ability to accept the love of God.

The Process of Total Acceptance

Acceptance by God   Like every long journey, the involvement in this theology begins with the first step down the road toward total acceptance. It is the most crucial step, for without it the journey toward fulfillment is never completed. The "good news," which is the Christian gospel, says loudly and clearly and without equivocation that every man is acceptable to God. The significance of this declaration has somehow been buried in the volumes and tomes of ecclesiastical dogmas, hidden from the ordinary man. Furthermore, this theological ignorance, or the unawareness of God's acceptance of every human creature can, to a large extent, be credited to the church's preoccupation with organization and denominationalism while neglecting a concern for the individual member. Unfortunately, a misconception has been created and fostered by many exponents of the traditional Christian faith that would imply that there are certain contingencies surrounding this acceptance of man by God. This is not the case. Man is acceptable to God precisely as he is. His acceptance is in no way predicated upon a change of life style or even upon the promise of repentance. Only in the sense that acceptance by God requires that each potential recipient put forth the effort of receiving this acceptance is there any demand placed upon the individual. A gift that is never received is of no value; acceptance by God becomes real only when the gift is received.

Acceptance of God   Acceptance of God is quite a different matter from God's acceptance of us, and the nature of this form of acceptance is largely determined by the individual's response to the accepting love of God. Again we reiterate the sequential pattern that develops after the initial acceptance by God. It takes this course: first, there is an awareness of responsibility and guilt; second, gaining God's forgiveness; and third, making a commitment to God.

Martin Buber says, "There is no responsibility unless there is one to whom one is responsible, for there is no response where there is no address. "[34] We first must recognize our responsibility to God before we become aware of our guilt. Herein lies the mechanism for guilt in a theological framework. From the moment of our acceptance by God, we gradually become aware of a responsibility to someone higher than self and society. As a result, we begin to see ourselves as we actually are as well as what we ought to be. It is the recognition of the vast difference between our being and our potential that produces many of our guilt feelings. We recall segments of our past and present lives that show us how we have deprived others as well as ourselves of the joy of living. Moreover, we begin to see how we have wasted many opportunities to develop our God-given talents through self-indulgence and slovenly action. And once we have become aware that life is really a gift from God and that we are held responsible for its use and development, we begin to feel our guilt.

The awareness of responsibility is therefore the precursor for the production of guilt feelings. And, an awareness of guilt becomes the forerunner for our recognition of the need for forgiveness. Feeling guilt makes us painfully uncomfortable—and we soon discover that only an act of forgiveness will eradicate these feelings of guilt. Our guilt also alerts us to the recognition that we are separated from the Source of forgiveness.

The process of obtaining God's forgiveness can be divided into three rather specific steps: asking, receiving, and accepting. The means is usually through prayer and service. In most instances it is necessary to ask God's pardon for our specific actions or nonactions that have contributed to our separation from him. Asking, therefore, becomes the imperative for receiving. But asking alone is not enough. It is the sincerity, the quality, and perhaps to some extent the persistence of the asking that may make the difference between receiving and not receiving. And it must be remembered that it is not so important how we ask as it is that we ask.

Furthermore, it must be understood that God's forgiveness is not automatic. Nor is it forthcoming upon demand. God very actively participates in the decision of when and how he offers his forgiveness. But it is never a question of "if." His willingness to forgive is ever-present; it is merely a matter of when. It must also be understood that the receiving of forgiveness is always out of the abundance of God's grace, and never a matter of convincing God of our right to be forgiven.

The final step in forgiveness is the process of accepting. Without the acceptance of God's forgiveness, the act of forgiveness is never complete. This is perhaps the most difficult fact concerning God's pardon. Many cannot believe that God does offer an unqualified and unlimited forgiveness for any act or nonact for which we are responsible. This would include the full spectrum of human atrocities, even the denial of the existence of God himself. This is why God's love will always remain incomprehensible. But man's refusal to accept God's forgiveness renders him incapable of freeing himself from his guilt.

It must be understood that forgiveness does not erase man's responsibility for his wrongful act or nonact, nor does it remove the possibility of punishment. Neither God's justice nor human justice can ignore certain wrongdoings. But the phenomenon of forgiveness offers release from the grip of guilt and freedom from all of its destructive potential. So while forgiveness does not release man from his responsibility, the joy of God's forgiveness can make even the most severe punishment tolerable.

The gift of forgiveness is also the gift of freedom—freedom from the destructiveness of guilt. It is a freedom that allows the individual to choose his own mode of expression and direction for his existential life without being intimidated by popular opinion. When one has become the joyful recipient of God's forgiveness, he has become emancipated from human enslavement. Instead of being someone's boy, he becomes a servant only to God. Yet here is a seeming paradox. Cannot man only serve God by serving man? The answer is obviously yes. All those who genuinely and maturely love God must serve God's creatures, but in a manner that is pleasing to God and not necessarily in keeping with the dictates of man.

Oddly enough, everyone does not want the gift of freedom. Albert Camus became aware of this cleverly disguised fact and reveals it eloquently in the final chapter of his novel *The Fall.* He says,

> Without slavery, as a matter of fact, there is no definitive solution. . . . I didn't know that freedom is not a reward or a decoration that is celebrated with champagne. Nor yet a gift, a box of dainties designed to make you lick your chops. Oh, no! It's a chore, on the contrary, and a long-distance race, quiet, solitary and very exhausting. No champagne, no friends raising their glasses as they look at you affectionately. Alone in a forbidding room, alone in the prisoner's box before the judges, and alone to decide in face of oneself or in the face of others judgment. At the end of all freedom is a court sentence; that's why freedom is too heavy to bear, especially when you're down with a fever, or are distressed or love nobody. . . . In short, you see, the essential is to cease being free and to obey, in repentance, a greater rogue than oneself.[35]

God makes demands upon those who choose to serve him, and freedom and responsibility are two such conditions, which brings us to the subject of commitment. Commitment is the degree of dedication one chooses to adopt in his relationship to God. But God makes other significant demands in addition to the gift of freedom and the demand of responsibility. These are perhaps best summed up in an extension of the Hebrew's Shema, or what some members of the Christian faith refer to as "God's absolute imperatives." They are: "Love the Lord your God with all your heart, with all your soul, with all your mind," and "Love your neighbor as yourself."[36] These are considered by many Jews and Christians alike to represent God's supreme and unequivocal commandments, and adherence to these is required of all those who truly seek spiritual health and desire to maintain close union with their Creator.

There are numerous examples in both secular and sacred literature of God's constant call for commitment and man's varying response. One literary illustration of this interaction is in Hesse's *Steppenwolf*. Hesse is expressing man's common tendency to make a partial or compromising commitment to God, to repel his offer for freedom, and to shirk his existential responsibility. He has Harry Haller say:

Now what we call "bourgeois," when regarded as an element always to be found in human life, is nothing else than the search for a balance. It is the striving after a mean between the countless extremes and opposites that arise in human conduct. If we take any one of these coupled opposites, such as piety and profligacy, the analogy is immediately comprehensible. It is open to a man to give himself up wholly to spiritual views, to seeking after God, to the ideal of saintliness. On the other hand, he can equally give himself up entirely to the life of instinct, to the lust of the flesh, and so direct all of his efforts to the attainment of momentary pleasures. The one path leads to the saint, to the martyrdom of the spirit and surrender to God. The other path leads to the profligate, to the martyrdom of the flesh, the surrender to corruption. Now it is between the two, in the middle of the road, that the bourgeois seems to walk. He will never surrender himself either to lust or to asceticism. He will never be a martyr or agree to his own destruction. On the contrary, his ideal is not to give up but to maintain his own identity. He strives neither for the saintly nor its opposite. The absolute is his abhorrence. He may be ready to serve God, but not by giving up the fleshpots. He is ready to be virtuous, but likes to be easy and comfortable in this world as well. In short, his aim is to make a home for himself between two extremes in a temperate zone without violent storms and tempests; and in this he succeeds though it be at the cost of that intensity of life and feeling which an extreme life affords. A man cannot live intensely except at the cost of the self. Now the bourgeois treasures nothing more highly than the self (rudimentary as his may be). And so at the cost of intensity he achieves his own preservation and security. His harvest is a quiet mind which he prefers to being possessed by God, as he does comfort to pleasure, convenience to liberty, and a pleasant temperature to that deathly inner consuming fire. The bourgeois is consequently by nature a creature of weak impulses, anxious, fearful of giving himself away and easy to rule. Therefore, he has substituted majority for power, law for force, and the polling booth for responsibility.[37]

Thomas Kelly, a Quaker mystic, provides us with another illustration of what could be man's highest response to God's unselfish love:

Meister Eckhart wrote: "There are plenty to follow our Lord halfway, but not the other half. They will give up possessions, friends and honors, but it touches them too closely to disown themselves." It is just this astonishing life which is willing to follow Him the other half, sincerely to disown itself, this life which intends *complete* obedience, without *any* reservations, that I would propose to you in all humility, in all boldness, in all seriousness. I mean this literally, utterly, completely, and I mean it for you and for me— commit your lives in unreserved obedience to Him. If you don't realize the revolutionary explosiveness of this proposal, you don't understand what I mean. Only now and then comes a man or a woman who, like John Woolman or Francis of Assisi, is willing to be utterly obedient, to go the other half, to follow God's faintest whisper. But when such a commitment comes in a human life, God breaks through, miracles are wrought, world-renewing divine forces are released, history changes. There is nothing more important now than to have the human race endowed with just such committed lives.[38]

A third expression of Christian commitment to God is defined by Dietrich Bonhoeffer:

We can only achieve perfect liberty and enjoy fellowship with Jesus when his command, his call to absolute discipleship, is appreciated in its entirety. Only the man who follows the command of Jesus single-mindedly, and unresistingly, lets his yoke rest upon him, finds his burden easy, and under its gentle pressure receives the power to persevere in the right way. The command of Jesus is hard, unutterably hard, for those who try to resist it. But for those who willingly submit, the yoke is easy, and the burden is light. "His Commandments are not grievous" (I John 5.3). The commandment of Jesus is not a sort of spiritual shock treatment. Jesus asks nothing of us without giving us the strength to perform it. His commandment never seeks to destroy life, but to foster, strengthen and heal it.[39]

These are the essential steps in the process of acceptance of God. Once this has been achieved, the maturing person is able to move on to self-acceptance.

Acceptance of Self   Telotherapy readily agrees with humanistic psychology that self-acceptance is not altogether determined by one's harmonious relationship with God, for most people acquire a certain degree of self-acceptance without having experienced a known encounter with their Creator. But telotherapy does say that only those who have developed a close union with God and have made a commitment to serve him will ever be able to reach their highest pinnacle of self-acceptance. I believe there is ample evidence for this assumption if one is willing to accept, a priori, the basic truths expressed in the theological doctrines of the Christian faith.

Most psychologists would likely concur that three of the major impediments to self-acceptance lie within the destructive elements of guilt, and hostility toward one's self and others. Each of these can be effectively eradicated through the application of telotherapy. Applied psychology, on the other hand, can never completely remove or resolve guilt, nor can it effectively erase hostility. Love is the only effective antidote for all three of these conditions. And because God is the ultimate source of all love, the patient must somehow align himself with God in order to receive this healing power. Modern psychology attempts to diminish the harmful effects of these three destructive elements by either rearranging the patient's value system, by adding flexibility to his superego, or by utilizing different defense mechanisms to replace his ineffective ones. This maneuvering may temporarily reduce the patient's suffering, but it seldom produces the lasting relief most patients so desperately seek.

Self-acceptance is made possible for all those who are united with God, because they know that if God finds them to be acceptable, they can accept themselves.

Acceptance of Others   This final form of acceptance offers the greatest chance for accord between telotherapists and psychotherapists. Both disciplines would generally agree that an individual's ability to accept others depends mainly upon his acceptance of himself. Although a certain degree of other-acceptance can be accomplished with only a limited amount of self-acceptance, there seems to be more than a slight suggestion of a direct corollary between the two. The question of how you can love others if you can't love yourself is still valid.

It is difficult for me to see how white people will ever be able to accept black people, rich people to accept poor people, or strong people to accept weak people and vice versa unless each person in each category first learns to accept himself. And anyone whose self-acceptance does not begin in being accepted by and of God will seldom if ever look upon someone of another race, another economic bracket, or of differing physical or intellectual strength as deserving equal love and concern. Here again it would seem that applied Christianity, or telotherapy, has the edge over humanistic psychology, for it is infinitely easier to love others of all kinds, shapes, and sizes if one's own self-acceptance is founded upon an awareness that everyone is accepted equally by God.

Total acceptance, therefore, has as its essential components acceptance by and of God, acceptance of self, and acceptance of others. Each plays a vital role in the total process of healing and maturation.

The Abundant Life

Between acceptance and fulfillment lies the full spectrum of meaningful human existence. Within the context of the Christian faith, this expression of living is referred to as the abundant life. The hallmark of those who live the abundant life is that each participant lives for others and thereby becomes a servant to mankind.

If we were to offer the names of such men as Pope John XXIII, Mahatma Gandhi, Albert Schweitzer, and Martin Luther King, Jr., most people would agree that they are outstanding examples of those who lived for others. And if we added the names of contemporary men like Father James Groppi, Jesse Jackson, Charles Evers, Ralph Nader, and Cesar Chavez, at least some of the more magnanimous people would classify them as men who give unstintingly of themselves in order to make life better for others. But how many would be willing to include the names of Huey Newton, Eldridge Cleaver, or Daniel and Philip Berrigan? Yet by our definition, each of these men would qualify as full members in the fraternity of those who live for others. Many people tend to forget that Jesus—the supreme example of "a man for others"—was crucified for treason by the proponents of law and order. It was Jesus' harsh and frequent criticism of the corrupt legal and religious practices in the leadership of the Jewish community that precipitated his death.

I believe it is also necessary to comment upon some of the personality traits of those who participate in the abundant life. Too often we think of these persons as always being calm, peaceful, serene, and imperturable, when in fact they are often tense, angry, frustrated, and disappointed. What we are seeing are their ambivalent moods: joy and sorrow, serenity and frustration, peacefulness and anger. A moment's reflection will tell us why. Their joy is in their awareness of the sustaining love of God, but their sorrow is for those who refuse to accept God's love. Their serenity is in the knowledge that "in everything, as we know, he co–operates for good with those who love God and are called according to his purpose."[40] But they are humanly impatient and cannot always envision how this will actually come about. And their peace is founded in the peace of God, but their anger arises from their awareness of the exploitation and injustices foisted upon the poor by the wealthy, the ignorant by the crafty, and the weak by the strong. So few of these men fit the placid and benign stereotype of a "gentle Jesus, meek and mild," which even Jesus did not.

Karl Barth captures the essence of the abundant life in his statement, "We are in the world not to comfort ourselves but to comfort others."[41] Jesus put it even more forcefully when he said, "If anyone wishes to be a follower of mine, he must leave self behind; he must take up his cross and come with me."[42] Neither statement would suggest that participating in the abundant life is always an easy or a joyful task. Yet paradoxical as it may seem, only those who are willing to become involved in this intense life will be able to experience the abundant joy of a meaningful existence.

I have on the wall of my office a copy of Henry Goldschmidt's "Life Inventory." It says, "Did you live? How much plowing did you do? How many loaves of bread did you bake for men? How much sewing did you do? How many trees did you plant? How many bricks did you lay in building ere you left? How much warmth did you give? What was your service?" It is hanging there to remind me, as well as my patients, that our answers to these questions may represent the true means by which we should measure the effectiveness of our lives.

Fulfillment

Fulfillment is the climax of creation. It has both universal and individual significance. Universally, fulfillment is the consummation of history and the advent of the arrival of the Kingdom of Heaven. Individually, fulfillment is participation in Eternal Life. It begins with the acceptance of God's love and ends with the gift of ultimate salvation; it is a promise kept.

It is almost impossible to go much beyond this point in defining the nature or concept of fulfillment, for it is experienced only in Eternal Life, the third and final phase of total life. Anything more specific than this, according to Tillich, would fall into the realm of "poetic imagination." Yet fulfillment is a goal worth striving toward, a pearl more valuable than its price. It must always exceed man's grasp but not his expectation, or it would be a goal unworthy of man's effort and a gift beneath the diginity of God.

The theology of acceptance and fulfillment, therefore, becomes the alpha and omega. Meaningful existence begins at the moment of acceptance of God's love and ends in its fulfillment. And between these two poles man participates in the often joyful and fulfilling expression of the abundant life by serving both God and man.

7
The Future of Telotherapy

Above all else, the Church must become an oasis of love within the vast deserts of human hostility and despair. If it fails in this task, there will be a diminished hope for mankind and little or no need for the Church.[43]

The future of telotherapy lies almost exclusively in the hands of the clergy and those interested in approaching the problem of emotional illnesses from a predominantly theological rather than a psychological perspective. It would be the rare psychologist or psychiatrist who would even acknowledge the possible merit of this analysis and therapeutic approach to what he calls nonorganic mental illness. The reluctance of these therapists is due mainly to their lack of awareness of the inherent spiritual nature of man. Therefore they are unable to see any reason to accept or even to consider the likelihood that man's emotional illness might arise from a tenuous or ruptured relationship between God and the suffering individual. Thus the future of this unique form of therapy becomes both the challenge and the responsibility of the members of the clergy.

Telotherapy must first of all develop its own identity as a separate means of treating people who are suffering from emotional or spiritual illness. This must be done primarily by the clergy themselves. It should not be undertaken in cooperation with psychologists and psychiatrists during the initial phase of its development, for it would have little chance to succeed. There is a tendency for the old to dominate the new and for the strong to consume the weak. So anything new or revolutionary must first learn to stand on its own merit rather than lean heavily on that which has proved to be relatively successful. Telotherapy is no exception. It must initially prove itself worthy to become an equal participant in the fraternity of the healing arts before it can effectively lend its uniqueness to that which already exists without running the risk of sacrificing its own identity.

One of the many ways that a program for training telotherapists could be started is through the establishment of an Academy of Telotherapy. This academy would be comprised of those theologians, pastoral ministers, priests, physicians, and interested laymen who recognize the frequency and severity of spiritual illness and who believe in the tremendous healing potential of telotherapy.

A course of study could be developed that would train individuals with a theological background in the techniques and skills necessary to administer telotherapy. The logical place for its academic inception would be in the theological seminaries, where a curriculum could be designed to meet several levels of need. One level of training could be for the seminary student who desires to specialize in telotherapy and who wants to devote most of his time and energy to the healing ministry. A second level could be structured for those entering the general parish ministry who do not want to specialize in just the healing aspect of the Christian faith but who nevertheless want to have some knowledge of and experience with telotherapy. And there would be a third level for the ministers and priests already engaged in the general parish ministry, but who could return to receive further training in order to more effectively help their parishioners who suffer from spiritual illness. Furthermore, I would suggest that the highest level of training should be of sufficient academic excellence to qualify the student for a doctorate degree in clinical theology; those with lesser training would receive a different form of recognition and designation. Uniform standards for academic achievement would have to be established by the Academy of Telotherapy or by the seminary responsible for the course of instruction. Courses in pastoral psychology could be continued as long as they taught the basic dynamics of existential or humanistic psychology.

Of necessity, this curriculum for telotherapists should also include introductory courses in psychiatry, which would acquaint the clinical theologian with the various modes of diagnosis utilized by psychoanalysts and psychotherapists. The telotherapist should become acquainted with the pharmacological actions of the various medications used in psychiatry, even though he would not be licensed to prescribe them. And he should become knowledgeable about the effects of electroshock, hydrotherapy, insulin shock, hypnosis, and other commonly used methods of psychiatric treatment. Basic knowledge about the many forms of mental illness that have an organic basis should also be included in this course of study.

But it should be emphasized that telotherapy does not compete with psychology and psychiatry in the treatment of those who suffer from the most severe forms of nonorganic mental illness, except in a supporting capacity. Telotherapy recognizes that psychiatry presently offers the greatest therapeutic hope for most persons afflicted with major forms of organic or nonorganic mental illness, especially in those cases where there is loss of contact with reality. Failure on the part of the telotherapist to be cognizant of this fact would constitute a grave error in his understanding of the limits of telotherapy. In the future, however, it is hoped that telotherapists will be called in consultation by the psychiatrist to assist in treating even these more seriously ill patients when contact with reality had been restored or to offer supportive therapy to those unable to overcome their psychosis.

Telotherapy could also become instrumental in the reorganization of the church. It could help the church become an institution of healing as well as one of teaching and serving. How could this be accomplished? First, the church must be willing to undergo both rapid and radical changes in order to become a more meaningful and potent force in our society. This fact has been voiced by clergymen on nearly every parish and church-institutional level. Most of these visionaries agree that giant strides must be taken toward church consolidation. Initially, as well as realistically, they believe it must begin *within* the various denominations before it can gain the momentum to spread *between* denominations. They advocate that the Church must be willing to sell its buildings and property that are no longer needed to implement an effective ministry. Eventually, geographic consolidation that crosses both denominational and divisional (Catholic and Protestant) lines should become a reality. This would make it possible to fulfill the spiritual needs of specific areas within each community at the lowest possible cost and at the greatest convenience. This painful but necessary process of consolidation would have to also include all equipment, professional and ancillary staff, and financial resources. It would eventually have to be a total amalgamation.

On the basis of these proposed organizational changes, I have envisioned the possibility of the following alterations within the local church. Each consolidated church would need a minimum of four primary professional personnel: one church administrator and three other ordained priests or ministers, each of whom would be trained in a special capacity but with interlocking and complementary skills. The administrator would be responsible for the operation and maintenance of the church buildings, property, and equipment. Moreover, his responsibilities would include the scheduling of weddings, funerals, and baptisms as well as fund-raising through pledges and donations from the church membership. The administrator would be the designated chairman of the board of trustees, a member of the official board, and placed in charge of the total operational budget. In this way the three ministers would be free of all the above responsibilities, and would be less encumbered to do the work for which they were best qualified.

Each ordained minister, as we have said, should be trained as a specialist. He would have developed this expertise through his seminary training in one of the three avenues of ministerial effort: the ministry of teaching, the ministry of serving, or the ministry of healing.

The Ministry of Teaching

In most Protestant churches theological knowledge is disseminated through two primary mediums: the Sunday sermon and the church school classroom teaching. In the sermon, the period of instruction lasts for approximately twenty minutes; within the classroom, the actual duration of study seldom exceeds thirty minutes. And, as noted earlier, most volunteers who organize and participate in this teaching program have limited qualifications. The Catholic church, on the other hand, are somewhat more diligent in their teaching efforts. It promotes, and makes mandatory, a rather intensive course of instruction in Roman Catholic catechism for each of its communicants. It has long been proclaimed by the Catholic church, "Give me a child through the age of twelve and he will remain a Catholic for life." This bold and generally true statement, however, does not really assess the child's apprehension of theological truths as much as it reflects the effectiveness of his indoctrination to Catholicism.

Unfortunately, neither the Protestant nor the Catholic branches of the Christian faith have adequately developed courses of instruction for adults who wish to go beyond the perfunctory introduction to church doctrine and denominational differences. Few churches provide classes in which one can learn something about the personal and social application of central Christian beliefs or how to make one's religion relevant to his total life. This is indicative of one of the most flagrant educational deficiencies within our contemporary society.

Theology is a body of faith and knowledge that tells us not only about man's relationship to God, but also provides him with a concept about the meaning and purpose of life. One of the many duties of theology is to tell people how life ought to be in contradistinction to anthropology, sociology, and psychology, which tell them how life was or is. Furthermore, dynamic theology provides insight into the many ways one can move from life as it is to life as it ought to be. Yet this represents only a small portion of what theology has to offer those who seek its wisdom. This is the challenge for those who choose to participate in the teaching ministry; they must be able to make people aware of a need for this faith and knowledge and then assist them to attain it.

The present methods used to disseminate this theological wisdom are inadequate and relatively ineffective. We must therefore seek new ways to eliminate this paucity of theological knowledge, and teach people how to apply this faith and knowledge to their existential living. The solution to eradicating this widespread theological ignorance lies principally within the realm of the teaching ministry. But the ministry must offer a new message, utilize new mediums, and develop new methods in order to resolve this urgent problem.

The message that I would propose is the same theology of acceptance and fulfillment we have already described. We must replace the traditional theology that espouses the corruptness of man, the atonement of Christ, and the need for salvation with a more contemporary one, one that emphasizes man's triple estrangement, his acceptance, and his opportunity for fulfillment. It is not that I disagree with many of the doctrinal concepts of traditional Christianity. It is a matter of recognizing that traditional theology fails to communicate the fundamental religious truth to the present generation. Traditional Christianity speaks in an archaic and foreign language to the members of the "now generation" and scarcely penetrates more than the most primitive level of their minds.

An exploration to find new ways to carry this new message is also challenging. But all new methods that fail to convey the new message are in themselves superfluous. It is the content of the message and not the means of communication that is of ultimate importance. Yet any message that is ineffectively communicated fails to achieve its purpose.

We should begin to search for new mediums by investigating the five modalities of human sensation: sight, hearing, taste, touch, and smell. Each one provides a potential medium for human communication.

Sight allows us to use art, literature, drama, dance, pantomime, television, motion and still pictures, and architecture to transmit a segment of theological wisdom in unique and separate ways. And to actually see a person who lives the exemplary Christian life can also help convey this new theology.

Touch allows us to feel physically loved and accepted by others who love and who are loved by God. The "laying on of hands," long a theological tradition, needs to be revitalized. Often a handshake, an arm about the shoulder, or a warm embrace can mediate the reality of acceptance in a way that no other means of communication can ever accomplish.

Hearing gives us the opportunity to listen to the wisdom of others: to teachers, to priests, to ministers, to professors, and to laymen who have discovered a portion of theological truth. Hearing makes possible the assimilation of these truths as well as allowing us to enjoy the sounds of music and of life.

Smell is such a primitive sensation that we often forget its potential in communication. Nearly every living thing emits a unique odor: a person, an animal, a leaf, or a flower. Even man-made things emit odors: automobiles, trains, buses, factories, and so forth. Some of these odors are repugnant to our sense of smell. But many convey the sweet scent of life in all of its majesty—sea air, country air, and city air. Every church sanctuary also has its own special aroma. Every hymnal, each pew, the alter candles, and each person who attends the service of worship contribute to this aroma. Theology is transmitted through the sense of smell insofar as it makes us aware that we are recipients and participants in God's creation.

Taste, together with smell, affords us the ability to enjoy the foods of our environment. Taste participates in the nourishment of our body and helps us to distinguish between what is good or bad for our consumption. The pleasure derived from eating good food, ingesting a cup of freshly brewed coffee, or taking a drink of clear cold water almost defies description. Taste can give us the joy and excitement of seeking different and better ways to procure and prepare both new and familiar foods. But the sense of taste should, above all else, make us keenly aware of those who have little or no food to enjoy and should stimulate us to share our abundant food with others.

There is yet a sixth sensory modality that is perhaps the most important of all. It is called extrasensory perception or, simply, ESP. Extrasensory perception is a metamodality, or one that exists above and beyond the other sensory modalities. It may actually be a fusion or synthesis of all of the other human sensations. Much interest has been centered in the peripheral powers attributed to ESP: its dimensions of clairvoyance and its potential to perceive the thoughts of another person, either living or dead. ESP also seems to operate as a complex receptor system that provides the individual with the ability to perceive and differentiate between nearly every form and intensity of human and divine stimuli: of being loved or unloved, of being accepted or rejected, of being fulfilled or unfulfilled. It is also this facet that most probably provides us with an inner sensitivity that contributes to our understanding of ourselves and of others. And it is this same mechanism that gives us much of our capacity to become aware of our relationship to God.

After enumerating the various mediums that are available for transmitting this new theology, we must discuss how we can apply new methods to them in order to improve the effectiveness of teaching theology.

In the beginning, we should change the way theology is taught in the church, its Sunday school, and in all private church-affiliated schools. Later it may be possible for theology to be taught in all public schools. But this will happen only when we have been able to remove the artificial division between secular and sacred teaching, and when there is no more fear of confrontation between church and state.

The program for teaching within the church (excluding private church-affiliated schools) should come under the direction of the person trained specifically for the teaching ministry. This ordained pastor should be given the authority not only to structure the Sunday morning sermon and the church school curriculum, but also to develop new and varied methods of teaching theology. This minister should have all of the latest and most effective educational equipment to allow him to successfully implement his teaching program. He should be given sufficient latitude and flexibility to make changes within the service of worship so as to be able to reach all age levels within the congregation without fear of reprisal or of losing support from the ruling body of the church.

Earlier I suggested that theology should ultimately be taught at all levels in the public schools. I believe that this is the only way everyone would be able to avail himself of the riches of theological wisdom. But because of the predictable opposition to this idea, all courses in theology would initially have to be optional. However, I would predict that once courses in theology became available, the demand for them would far exceed their availability. Who, young or old, would not like to learn something about creation and the meaning and purpose of life? But each time when one suggests that theological truths be taught within the public school system, the old specter of the separation of the church and state always reappears.

In all fairness, there is still something very valid and pertinent about this argument. Historically there has been a general mistrust between the ruling heads of state and the ruling heads of the church. Each wanted for himself complete and autonomous power over everything within his realm. First, it was the church who had the upper hand; later it was the state. When the church ruled supreme, the political ruler was totally subjugated to the wishes of the head of the church. And when the state gained control, it methodically usurped most of the power of the church as well as acquiring much of its material wealth. Today, there is still a tendency upon the part of some political rulers to want to control religion; and there are still some in the church's hierarchy who wish to regain some of its lost political strength. And it is partly because of this perpetual power struggle that the separation between church and state has been enforced in democratic societies.

Theology, therefore, must be taught on many levels and in many institutions so that man can learn how to resolve the problems of his existential predicament. And unless he learns the meaning and purpose of life, he will never find the joy and peace his heart desires. Man must learn of God in order to live effectively and to achieve fulfillment.

The Ministry of Serving

"So with faith; if it does not lead to action, it is itself a lifeless thing,"[44] says the author of the Book of James. If the church is to make any major contribution to contemporary society, it must get intimately involved in the problems of the world—locally, nationally, and internationally. This mature and ecumenical theology demands personal involvement in every condition that deprives one of God's children from the exuberance of living and the joy of being loved. This new message neither promotes nor condones the pseudoreligious philosophy of retreat, isolation, or escape from the problems that confront each segment of the human society.

But there seems to be a critical transitional phase between the process of acquiring theological knowledge and putting it into practice, which has to do with the difficult job of incorporating learned Christian ethics and precepts into one's lifestyle and value system. And the number of people who are able to make this transition are few.

Dr. Milton Rokeach, professor of psychology at Michigan State University, has observed this phenomenon. In 1968 he tried to determine whether the value system between the religiously devout and the nondevout differed in any appreciable or significant manner. He defines values as "our standards for living; they guide our conduct, lead us to take a particular position on a specific social issue, predispose us to favor one or another political ideology. They are standards we use to judge things, to praise or blame ourselves or others."[45] In the course of his study, he interviewed well over 1,000 adult Americans who ranged in age from 21 to 80 and who represented a cross section of all the various social, racial, religious, and economic strata of the country. After completing his survey, Rokeach made the following critical observations and expressed these conclusions.

The general picture that emerges from the results is that those who place a high value on salvation are conservative, anxious to maintain the status quo and unsympathetic to the black and the poor. They had reacted fearfully or even gleefully to the news of Martin Luther King's assassination, they are unsympathetic with student protests, and they do not want the church to become involved with the social or political issues of our society. . . . If hypocrisy is a discrepancy between a person's espoused values and his conduct and position on important contemporary issues, then these data from a representative sample of Americans strongly suggest a hypocrisy deeply embedded within many religiously oriented individuals. And by implication, the data point to a hypocrisy deeply embedded within organized religion as a social institution. . . . If the church taken as a whole, is at best irrelevant and at worst a training center for hypocrisy, indifference and callousness, it is unlikely that the clergy—members of the religious Establishment—will be the ones to initiate the program of radical change that seems to be called for. . . . Karl Marx proposed—with some justification, my data would suggest—that religion is the opiate of the people. But religion would be less open to the charge that it is an opiate if children were taught that salvation and happiness are the rewards for doing good rather than for not doing bad—for obeying the "thou-shalts" of the Sermon on the Mount rather than the "thou-shalt-nots" of the Ten Commandments. . . . Such a simple shift of focus, however, will probably require a profound reorganization of the total structure of organized Christianity. And if this reorganization does not come about, the data presented here lead me to propose that men will get along better with their fellow men if they can forget, or unlearn, or ignore what organized religion has taught them about values and what values are for.[46]

I am sure that most conscientious people will take umbrage to Rokeach's investigation and especially with his conclusions. Indeed, it seems to be a harsh indictment of organized religion. But we should be willing to recognize that much of what he says is generally true, if not always specifically valid. It should make us aware of the need to reorganize the teaching methods and teaching emphasis within the church. But even more important, his investigation points up the need to eliminate our hypocrisy and close the gap between religious thought and religious action. In other words, merely teaching theological truths is not enough. The church must be willing to spend sufficient time and effort in assisting its members to incorporate Christian principles within their total value system so that they will serve the people of their community with love, compassion, justice, and equality. And this duty should be shared equally between the ministers of teaching and the ministers of serving.

Today's problems are not obscure. They are patently and painfully obvious. The issues that threaten our individual and collective security, if not our very existence, include war, poverty, sickness, drug abuse, racial discrimination, social inequities and injustices, and environmental destruction. If this new theology for the Christian faith has little or nothing to offer in the way of a solution to these major threats other than a promise of "pie in the sky when you die," then theology is indeed irrelevant and deserves little or no allegiance. But if contemporary theology does have something to offer, then it must speak out.

The person who trains to become a minister of serving must, of necessity, have an exceptionally strong character. He must be willing and able to face opposition from within and without the church. Being a minister of serving will be neither as safe nor as comfortable as being a minister of teaching or of healing. It means getting the members of consolidated churches involved in attempting to resolve some of the major issues we have just mentioned. Some of the members must participate in the World Without War Council, whereas others should procure jobs and financial loans for unemployed people. This minister must encourage segments of his congregation to visit shut-ins, work in hospitals and free clinics, provide food and transportation in emergency situations, march in demonstrations for worthwhile causes, or act as peace marshalls in potentially explosive crowds. He must invite politicians, policemen, youthful dissenters, and conservationists to his church and let them speak to the membership so that they can learn both sides of the many issues that confront us. The role of the minister of serving can be exciting and fulfilling. But it must have an opportunity for growth, development, and expression, for it is one of the principal avenues through which religion can be made relevant.

The Ministry of Healing

Telotherapy is an expression of the healing ministry. I have attempted to develop a method of diagnosing and treating spiritual illness or the illness that arises from man's separation from God, himself, and others. The task of the telotherapist will be made easier if he works in close cooperation with the ministers of teaching and serving, for each one should become an integral part of the patient's therapy. And each patient must learn the basic concepts of theology in order to understand the dynamics of his illness and to appreciate the phenomenon of his healing. Each patient must also be willing to serve others if he is to gain the fulfillment or the *telos* he seeks.

Certainly telotherapy will not prove to be a panacea for all the problems which afflict the human race, many of which we have just discussed. But many of the major human problems—hatred and prejudice, greed and irresponsibility, fear and insecurity—reflect the presence of mass spiritual illness, one that has become compounded in the same way that individual evil is compounded into societal evil. And these combined evil forces serve to validate the frequency with which man perpetuates his separation from God and thereby produces the nidus for his spiritual illness. I believe that we could justifiably paraphrase the provocative statement by the wag who said, "Due to a lack of interest, tomorrow is cancelled" and say, "Due to a lack of love, humanity may not survive." Unfortunately, not enough people recognize the precariousness of man's predicament. Kierkegaard made this same observation when he wrote, "It happened that a fire broke out back stage in a theater. The clown came out to inform the public. They thought it was a jest and applauded. He repeated his warning, they shouted even louder. So I think the world will come to an end amid general applause from all the wits, who believe that it is a joke."[47]

I am sure it is the belief of nearly all clergymen that it is *agape*, the therapeutic love of God, that is most needed to heal the wounds of nations and to solve the problems of mankind. But human beings must convey the love of God to other human beings. And telotherapy is one way that the abstract love of God can be made concrete.

Many will immediately dismiss telotherapy by saying that it really contains nothing new or original. But have they recognized spiritual illness as a definite disease entity, or more important, recognized that spiritual and mental illness frequently coexist in the syndrome of human depression? And to those who would reject this concept of telotherapy, I would ask them to pose the following questions: Is telotherapy cogent? Is it valid? Is it relevant? And finally, does it work?

Telotherapy or its equivalent should survive for many reasons. First, it allows all the above questions to be answered in the affirmative. Second, the need for its therapeutic and curative potential is already in enormous demand. Third, it alone will be able to provide the definitive treatment for this dimension of human suffering. I am convinced that neither tranquilizers, antidepressants, stimulants, nor any present or future discoveries in psychology or clinical psychiatry will ever be able to offer more than palliative and temporary relief for spiritual illness.

Telotherapy can spring forth into the therapeutic arena or it can continue to lay substantially dormant. It has the inherent potential to develop into one of the greatest methods of human healing yet known to man. It, like no other therapeutic discipline, allows the love of God to flow virtually unimpaired into the parched and diseased recesses of the soul of man.

Notes

PROLOGUE

1. Teilhard de Chardin, *The Phenomenon of Man* (New York: Harper Torchbooks, 1965), pp. 283–84.

CHAPTER 1

2. Carl G. Jung, *Modern Man in Search of a Soul* (New York: Harcourt, Brace & Co., Harvest Books, 1933), pp. 192–93.
3. *Ibid.,* p. 228.
4. *Ibid.,* p. 240.
5. Erich Fromm, *The Art of Loving* (New York: Harper Row, 1956), p. 202.
6. David E. Roberts, *Psychotherapy and a Christian View of Man* (New York: Charles Scribner & Sons, 1950), p. 134.
7. Albert C. Outler, *Psychotherapy and the Christian Message* (New York: Harper & Row, Chapel Books, 1954), p. 253.

CHAPTER 2

8. Job 3:11, 20–22, RSV.
9. Hermann Hesse, *Steppenwolf* (New York: Holt, Rinehart and Winston, 1963), pp. 68–69.
10. Reinhold Niebuhr, *The Nature and Destiny of Man,* (New York: Charles Scribner's & Sons, 1941), 2:294.
11. Niebuhr, Ibid.

CHAPTER 3

12. By the author.
13. Frieda Fromm-Reichmann, *Principles of Intensive Psychotherapy* (Chicago: University of Chicago Press, 1950), p. 7.
14. Hesse, *Siddartha* (New York: New Directions, 1951), p. 85.
15. Jung, *Modern Man,* p. 234.
16. Outler, *Psychotherapy and the Christian Message,* p. 129.
17. Sigmund Freud, *The Defense of Neuropsychoses* in Selected Papers on Hysteria.

Nervous and Mental Disease Monograph Series, No. 4, N.Y.

18. Matthew 6:12, 14–15, NEB.

19. Paul Tillich, *Systematic Theology*, 3 vols. (Chicago: University of Chicago Press, 1951–63), 1:267.

20. Masnavi I Ma'navi, *The Spiritual Couplets of Jalalu-'D-Din Rimi*, trans. and abridged by E. H. Whinfield (London: Trubner & Co., 1887), II, vii, 82.

21. Matthew 26:39, NEB.

22. Gordon W. Allport, *The Individual and His Religion* (New York: Macmillan Co., Macmillan paperbacks, 1961), pp. 78–80.

23. Ephesians 6:13, RSV.

24. Roberts, *Psychotherapy and a Christian View of Man*, p. 135.

25. Sam Keen, *To a Dancing God* (New York: Harper & Row, 1970), p. 22.

CHAPTER 4

26. John J. Schwab, *Depression in Medical Practice* (Merck, Sharp and Dohme, 1970), p. 117.

27. Arthur P. Noyes and Lawrence C. Kolb, *Modern Clinical Psychiatry* (Philadelphia: W. B. Saunders Co., 1963), p. 81.

CHAPTER 5

28. Tillich, *Systematic Theology*, 1:3.

29. Outler, *Psychotherapy and the Christian Message*, p. 175.

30. Niebuhr, *The Nature and Destiny of Man* (New York: Charles Scribner & Sons, 1941), 2:294.

31. Outler, *Psychotherapy and the Christian Message*, p. 187.

32. Tillich, *Systematic Theology*, 3:299.

CHAPTER 6

33. Keen, *To a Dancing God*, p. 127.

34. Martin Buber, *The Way of Response* (New York: N. N. Glatzer, Schocken Books, 1966), p. 21.

35. Albert Camus, *The Fall* (New York: Random House, Vintage Books, 1956), pp. 132–33.

36. Matthew 22:37, 39, NEB.

37. Hesse, *Steppenwolf*, pp. 51–52.

38. Thomas Kelly, *A Testament of Devotion* (New York: Harper & Row, 1941), p. 52.

39. Dietrich Bonhoeffer, *The Cost of Discipleship* (New York: Macmillan Co., 1960), p. 31.

40. Romans 8:28, NEB.

41. Karl Barth, *Deliverance to the Captives* (New York: Harper & Row, 1961), p. 48.

42. Matthew 16:24, NEB.

CHAPTER 7

43. By the author.
44. James 2:17, NEB.
45. Milton Rokeach, "Faith, Hope and Bigotry," *Psychology Today* 3, no. 11 (April 1970):36.
46. *Ibid.*, p. 58.
47. Kierkegaard, *Either/Or* (Garden City, N.Y.: Doubleday Anchor Books, 1959), p. 30.